Careers in Caring

Careers in Caring

A Practical Guide to your First Job

GILL PHARAOH

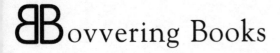
ovvering Books

Copyright © Gill Pharaoh 2010
First published in 2010 by Bovvering Books
11 Maple Mews, LONDON NW6 5UZ
www.yesiambovvered.co.uk

Distributed by Gardners Books, 1 Whittle Drive, Eastbourne,
East Sussex, BN23 6QH
Tel: +44(0)1323 521555 | Fax: +44(0)1323 521666

The right of Gill Pharaoh to be identified as the author of the work
has been asserted herein in accordance with the Copyright, Designs
and Patents Act 1988.

British Library Cataloguing in Publication Data
A catalogue record for this book is available from the British Library

ISBN 978-0-9562909-0-8

Typeset by Amolibros, Milverton, Somerset
www.amolibros.co.uk
This book production has been managed by Amolibros
Printed and bound by T J International Ltd, Padstow, Cornwall, UK

Acknowledgements

I would like to thank the following people for the part they have played in my life, which has led to this book being written.

First of all, Jack Curtin, a long-time colleague, who over time has supported so many of my ideas, helped me with many technicalities, and nagged me into writing nearly forty years ago.

Secondly, Maggs Herring, my "adopted daughter", who made me think about the role of the professional carer in the first place, and whose response to life has been a source of inspiration for more than twenty years.

And thirdly John, for all his help in assembling this book, and keeping my records as well as keeping his patience

And lastly, the many carers I have worked with over the years, with whom I have shared much laughter, some tears, and a great many memories.

Contents

Chapter One

What is a carer? Is this a new role?

This book has been written for the person who is thinking of starting a new career in caring. Every day the papers carry advertisements for carers, in the community, in homes for the elderly, or for chronically ill or disabled people of all ages, who want to stay in their own homes, and remain independent, for as long as they can. Few people want to end their lives in an institution, however pleasant it may be, and however tempting it sounds. Most people dread the thought of losing their home and their independence.

Caring as a job is not a new concept. There cannot be anyone who picks up this book who has not had some personal experience, or knowledge, of a carer.

Before nursing was a paid job or a career, in every community there were women who took care of the sick, women who performed last offices for the dying, women who helped mothers give birth, and women who used their breast milk to feed others' children. Some received money to perform these tasks, and some were following a family tradition, having watched and helped their mothers, or grandmothers, from an early age. Traditionally it seems that women have naturally accepted the role of the carer. What about the men?

Although so many of these helpers were women there were also men, many of them bone-setters, who had honed their skills on animals and graduated to people when the opportunity arose. There were also herbalists, again often a family tradition, to offer advice and treatment, much of which became tried and tested as medication, which, now assessed, patented, and developed, is still in use today.

All of these people developed communication skills, and as they handed down all they had learned the next generation became even more skilled and adept at making diagnoses and suggesting treatments.

At the latter end of the nineteenth century, when the effects of wars were more widely publicised, it became apparent that many people died of wounds that could have been treated. They died of disease, or shock, rather than on the battlefield. With the discovery that a lack of cleanliness seemed to be at the root of so many problems in healing, a new era seemed to be on the horizon. In a relatively short time we learned about anaesthetics, and then X-ray, and brave pioneers were instrumental in forging new standards of care for the sick.

Florence Nightingale is famous and in the mid-twentieth century many little girls wanted to emulate her, but she was only one of the many people who led the way.

There was a very famous nurse who has almost been forgotten, but who ought to be a shining example for the carers of today. Her name was Mary Seacole, a Jamaican woman born in 1805. Mary had a Scottish father, who was a doctor, and a Jamaican mother, who was a healer. Mary followed in her mother's footsteps, and, having married, practised her healing art on her many travels. After her husband died she applied to go to the Crimea, to help with the war effort. She was refused permission, and so she went without it, or indeed any help from the authorities, but became famous for her skill and care, and the service she provided the troops on the front line. When she finally returned to London, penniless and bankrupt, the country collected money to pay her debts in gratitude for all she had done. It is very well worth reading about this remarkable woman, who deserves a place in history. She is buried in St Mary's Cemetery in Kensal Green, in London. While writing this book I revisited the Florence Nightingale Museum in St Thomas's Hospital, and learned that it has now added the story of Mary to the exhibition of the Crimean War, and is giving her due credit for all that she did – only 100 years late!

For a long time, trained nurses were practice-based, and a large proportion of their training was devoted to practical or clinical issues. Inevitably, with the progress of medicine and technology, nurses needed more training and education to work more effectively, and a career structure developed, with the training becoming more and more academic. To an extent this has resulted in qualified nurses at one remove from the "hands-on" nature of the work, as treatments are more and more technical.

In the last fifty years, the increasing emphasis on an academic approach has resulted in the qualified nurse spending more of her time with management, which means more paperwork, and less time doing bed baths and routine general care. Hence the large growth in "carers", people who have not had the same training, but who can give the sort of practical care that a person who is sick cannot manage for themselves. Carers are no longer regarded as performing a slightly inferior role in the experience of the sick person, whether at home, or in the hospital or nursing home. They can complete a national vocational (NVQ) training course that will lead to a qualification, which means improved pay and working conditions. Among them are now many more men, because men make excellent and skilled carers and enjoy the work.

(This is the place to remind you, that if you have the chance to study for any of these qualifications at your place of work, then you should immediately grab it, and accept as much training as you can. It will not be wasted.)

So how do you know if you would like to do this kind of work? Are there special skills, and can you develop the skills you think you need? Well of course you can. We will look at the type of skills you need in the next chapters. Don't be intimidated by what you read – you may feel that you are being expected to become a cross between an angel and a qualified nurse overnight. This book is not a training course, or even part of one. I am writing on the assumption that most people who want to work with the sick want to do a good job. Your training can give you a clear idea of what you are aiming for, and hopefully, this book can give some more detailed ideas of what your patients, their families, and your own working colleagues would also appreciate. The aim is not to produce someone's idea of a perfect nurse, whatever that is, but to help you to do the job as well as you possibly can, and to enjoy doing it, and so develop the natural skills you already have. If you work at anything to the very best of your ability, you will get far more enjoyment out of it, and you will receive affection and appreciation and respect from your client group and from your colleagues. And if you have confidence in what you are doing, and how you are doing the job, you will enjoy the work more and do it more effectively.

Carers work in various environments. This book talks a lot about the carer in the home of the patient, but what it says can be applied to all carers, wherever they choose to work. Someone who has spent many years in an institution will regard their room in that place as their home.

If you are starting your career in a nursing home or somewhere similar, you may find it hard to see the patients as individuals, especially if the other staff members have been there a long time, or if you are working with someone who has not the same level of interest and enthusiasm, as (hopefully) you will have at the start of the job.

One of the first things you will realise about this kind of job is that every day is different. Certainly much of the work is the same, but every person you meet will be different. For some carers, even the place of work will change, as they work in the private homes of the client or patient. This means that initially you may find the work very tiring as you try to adapt to the individual.

Perhaps now I should explain that in the past we referred to the people we cared for as "patients". Nowadays the term used is "clients". I notice, however, that most of the carers I meet still call their clients their patients. So, mostly in this book, I will refer to "patients".

Margaret found the pace of work very fast indeed when she started at a small home for handicapped people. Her skills at communicating and building relationships seemed to be swamped by the rush of physical activity, as caring for these handicapped people ran to tight time schedules. The other carers had lost sight of the individuality of the patients, and simply wanted to finish each shift. It took some time to adjust to the pace, and to begin to deliver the level of personal holistic care she saw as essential for the well-being of the patients.

This is a very common reaction for someone starting this kind of work. So do not lose heart, and try not to be discouraged if you also feel overwhelmed at first. And if you like parts of the work, but perhaps not some of your colleagues, do not be afraid to look around for something more suited to your personality.

If you can develop some of the characteristics you are

reading about, you will be doing very well. On any one day you will never need to demonstrate all the qualities you read about. But over several contacts with different clients, or patients, you may well demonstrate many of them. What is very certain is that if you keep an open mind, and try to learn as you go, you will receive more enjoyment out of the work, more satisfaction and appreciation from all the people you have contact with, and therefore you will find the work less stressful.

Chapter Two

Basic hygiene

The first and probably most important attribute a carer needs is a good understanding of hygiene. This should not come as a surprise to you, because anyone who has had any experience of hospitals will have made observations as to hygiene standards evident in the ward they were in. Many ex-nurses are shocked and saddened at the lack of personal and clinical hygiene they believe exist in hospitals generally, because years ago the responsibility for the cleanliness of a ward or unit belonged to the nursing staff.

We read every day about some of the persistent infections around and the horror stories surrounding them. Most of the bacteria we hear about have lived and still live within, or on, our bodies without causing harm. The problems start when the bacteria have the opportunity to grow in the wrong place, at the wrong time. Many people who are admitted to hospital are discharged with something extra, something about which they know absolutely nothing. The name everyone recognises is MRSA, which is not caused by a new bacterium, but by one which has, over time, become resistant to many antibiotics. Hence the name "multi-resistant" *Staphylococcus aureas*.

Our response to any repeated infection is, obviously, to develop a stronger and more aggressive antibiotic. Since the bacteria causing the infection can often adapt very quickly, they recover, the infection returns, and the search begins again for a stronger antibiotic. And so the spiral continues.

You do not need to learn all about the various infections. You need to remember that if we all start taking simple steps towards improving our personal hygiene, there is strong evidence that this, and other problem bacteria, can be managed without them becoming multi-resistant to treatment with antibiotics.

In hospitals and clinics now you are asked to clean your hands with an antibacterial liquid before entering the clinical area. Cleaning your hands whenever you have handled body fluids is a major step in stopping the spread of infections. In the homes of your clients or patients, you need to remember that before you begin, and as soon as you finish a personal task for anyone, a good wash with soap and hot water is essential. If you are caring for someone who has just been discharged from hospital, be especially careful. You do not need disinfectants – just a thorough scrub in *hot* soapy water. As we have seen, we commonly carry many bacteria on our persons, which only become a problem when they invade different parts of our bodies, and develop a resistance to antibiotics.

Even as I was writing this, there was a radio announcement about a hospital that claims it has eliminated MRSA, not with "wonder drugs" but with plain old-fashioned scrubbing with soap and hot water.

Personal hygiene also includes the clothes you wear, the shoes and the uniform. We are going on to discuss this later in this chapter.

Our skin is designed to deal with a multitude of bacteria, both good and bad. It is a fashion now to use complex disinfectants in the shower, on kitchen surfaces, or on the spot on your face, or a graze on your knee. The result of overuse of disinfectants is that they eventually become less effective. So using them too frequently means that in time we will need something stronger.

The HIV virus (human immunodeficiency virus) is also destroyed quickly by hot water and soap. So is the *E coli* (*Escherichia coli*) bacterium, which causes illness and death, when it affects old frail people or children, or someone with an impaired immune response. It lives in our intestines, where it causes no problems at all. But leave it on your hands after a visit to the toilet, and then handle food, and it can wreak havoc.

So before you think about anything to do with caring, remember your basic hygiene. Protect your vulnerable clients or patients by keeping your own bacteria to yourself, and protect your family by not taking home with you any extra "bugs". All you need is regular use of hot water and some soap.

When you are travelling from home to work, or vice versa, on public transport and often via the shops, you will need to wash your hands when you arrive at your destination. This is not at all neurotic since you have no idea of the standards or conditions of the other people who have passed along your route before you.

Any equipment you use, and any surfaces you use, while you are in someone's house, are a potential source of infection. Without becoming paranoid, get into the habit of working in a clean manner. If there are gloves in the house for your use, use them. Make sure soiled equipment is disposed of correctly. Do not be tempted to cut corners.

Years ago nurses were not allowed to wear their uniforms in public places, so that wearing outdoor coats was mandatory. There were good reasons for this, and one of them was to limit the spread of infection. Now that it is not uncommon to see nurses in uniform, stopping off in pubs and supermarkets, you need to ensure that you change your uniform daily, and that you are aware of the effects your behaviour may have in your place of work.

Paul's story is typical of many. He went into hospital for a major treatment for lymphoma, which is a type of cancer of the lymph glands. He was there for months because the treatment for this illness always results in damage to the immune system. Usually, the treatment requires nursing the patient in a single room, and ensuring that anyone entering the room is masked, wears an apron, and washes their hands on coming in or leaving. This includes friends and family, as well as staff. His friends and family faithfully did as they were told.

His wife was therefore surprised when she observed qualified nurses popping in and out to do checks, without taking any of the precautions. Not only that, she picked up soiled dressings from the floor on several occasions, soiled bed linen regularly, and stale food left for hours at a time. Although he had a private bathroom he often needed to use a bedpan, as he felt too ill and weak to get up. His used bedpan attracted flies while it waited to be removed. Unable to clean himself after one bout of diarrhoea, he remained in a dirty state, until his wife arrived to clean him up. The distress caused to him and his family can only be imagined.

He developed several infections, which were opportunistic in the sense that they could not have got a foothold on a healthy person who had a good immune system, but easily entered the body of someone who had low immunity.

He also developed quite severe depression. Think of the situation as he saw it. He felt and *was* very ill. He was ill in an environment totally unlike the one in which he lived. Unable to clean himself, he felt useless, and his self-esteem was at a low ebb. He had always been a well-groomed man, and was ashamed when friends came to see him in such a situation. He was angry and humiliated, and his wife was embarrassed, and was not always comfortable with the level of care she felt she had no choice but to give him. She could not have left him in such a state. She and Paul were very close and she was glad to care for him, but he had to depend on her far more than he should have, considering that he was a sick man in a hospital bed, and might have expected to receive better nursing care. She was torn between wanting to care for him, but not wanting to take on the role of chief nurse, preferring the position of wife, with all the intimacy and communication that should have resulted from less stressful times together. After he died, she could not forget the memories of the poor care he received at the hands of qualified staff. Learning that he had MRSA among his other problems did not help her emotional state, though that was not what caused his death.

Anti-depressants are of no use when the cause of the depression is identified and understood, yet remains unrelieved, in a situation that is out of the control of the person who's depressed, and within the control of his professional carers. There are many professionals who believe that good self-esteem is essential when you have a compromised immune system. It has been shown that people with AIDS (acquired immunodeficiency syndrome) live longer if they can boost their confidence, and look after themselves. You cannot do that if you are lying in a dirty bed in a dirty room.

Of course you cannot start cleaning up all the houses you visit. And you cannot impose your own standards of hygiene on other people on the basis that you are right, and everyone else is wrong. Many of the houses you visit may not meet the standards you set in your own home. But you can clean up after yourself, and not leave the place in a worse state than when you arrived. You will boost the mood of your patient as well as giving good care.

Over the next few chapters we are going to look at some of the other skills and attributes you can develop over time, which will enable you to become a good carer. As we have said, this will not only benefit your patients, but more than that will enable you to get the most enjoyment and satisfaction from the job you have chosen. That is very important. It is so rare today to meet someone who can say that they love their job, and would not change it for any other. A life spent caring for the sick or disabled can offer the kind of satisfaction that is a joy to look back on.

Chapter Three

The temperament of a carer

You do not need to be a saint to become a carer. In fact a down-to-earth approach is both easier for you to maintain, and much easier for other people to live with. But you do need to be aware of, and in control of, your behaviour, so that you can monitor your responses in times of stress.

If you lose your temper with the general public, and throw things, or swear at people, you will have trouble controlling your temper with sick and anxious people, and their families.

Whether you arrive somewhere, furious with the traffic, cross with the lateness of the bus, impatient with your family before you left home, mad with your boss because you have not been given adequate information or support, or if you have just got out of bed on the wrong side and have a headache, know that you can start every one of your patients on a long lonely day.

Culturally, in the past in Britain, it has been rather unacceptable to lose your temper publicly. The old stiff upper lip has been promoted across the range of emotions. The softening of this attitude has been a good thing in many ways, and we have learned that it is healthy to show emotion and affection. However there has also been a trend of violence that is not attractive, and not healthy, but all too often shows a lack of understanding of the problems faced by less fortunate people.

Sick people, and stressed families, are not easy to work with, and can be exasperating for the carer. It is quite reasonable for you to mark boundaries, and to expect certain standards of behaviour from your patient or client. It is not reasonable to expect that you will always find it easy. We will look at this later in this chapter.

Most people respond to a funny situation, even at times of great stress. Carers are often accused of developing a macabre sense of humour. This is because humour is a great way of releasing or diffusing tension. You cannot be a permanent wit, but just be aware of the potential. If you can see the funny side of a situation, you will never find the stress builds up as much. It is a bonus if you have the chance to share your amusement with someone at the time.

Cilla was an untidy, often disorganised carer, who always had some misadventure on her way to work. However, she managed to make her disaster stories short and very funny, and mostly her audience were very amused by them. She gave people something to think about, and they chuckled about her when she had gone, and shared their amusement with friends. She did her work efficiently, and could tell her stories while she worked. And she seemed to know when to be quiet and when to chat.

Polly on the other hand had many personal problems, and talked freely about them all to her patients and their families. The reaction was mixed. Some people became bored with the detail, and depressed by her gloom-and-doom approach; some people became too involved and very anxious for her, and even felt guilty about her salary, and her financial commitments; some found her intimacy very embarrassing.

Resist the temptation to confide in your patients any of your problems, whether financial or emotional. That is not to say that you tell them nothing at all. It is easy to be seen as very lucky, and perhaps a little bit removed from real life, by your patients. From their point of view you are indeed lucky. You have your health, a job, maybe a car, and somewhere outside your work they imagine you are leading a nice life. You can tell them that you are divorced, that you are buying your house, or that your child is not doing well at school, but don't go into the financial details, or make it all sound hopeless and as if you're having trouble coping, even if you are.

Many people with disabilities *are* very well able to laugh at situations that able-bodied folk find it hard to understand at all. We can only admire them. It is perhaps easier to laugh and to feel optimistic if your disability is not getting progressively worse. This may be why old people are difficult to care for, since for most of them things are only going to get more difficult. They are only too aware that there is not too much to look forward to, that they are not going to recover their strength, start a new family, or a new job, or have another big holiday. You cannot offer them much more than to show you have some awareness and understanding of their situation, and perhaps make them smile. You can always join in if they are amused at something, but do not laugh *at* them, only ever *with* them.

Similarly, when you know someone very well, you can gently tease them sometimes. You cannot often tease confused and disorientated people, however tempting it is. In fact you can add to their confusion, so be very careful in your conversations with someone who is confused. Try to be reassuring, but do not encourage their confusion by agreeing with all they say. This can be difficult, as for example when someone tells you her mother is coming and she obviously thinks she is still a child. Remind her of the realities in as gentle a manner as possible, without raising your voice or appearing to confront her.

Most important of all, never discuss your patients with any other patient. Of course you can say that you have met someone else with a similar situation, or yes, you have come across a particular disease before, but never give any details that could identify the person. And never give out gloomy news, such as "Yes, I knew someone with your disease once, but he's dead." You may laugh at the idea that you could be so insensitive, but it does happen!

Confidentiality is a tremendous issue for most people and many carers are in a position of great trust. Sick people who are lonely can be vulnerable and will be inclined to trust you, the carer, with very personal information. This happens especially if you are sympathetic, and they like you. Keep it to yourself.

Similarly be careful in public places. On one occasion a nurse was sitting on a train in London, when she became aware of a group of young women talking together. They were quite loud, and she suddenly realised that they were all nurses, and were talking about someone she also knew, but was not aware that the person was in hospital. She recognised the family situation of the woman they were talking about, though she was a few miles from the hospital location. She asked the group on which ward did they work, as she would like to visit the patient they were discussing. They were all mortified and immediately stopped the conversation, and got off at the next stop. I know this story is true because I was that nurse on the train. Perhaps I should have reported them, but I was very young, and so were they, and they were very shocked at what I said, so I just hoped that they had learned a lesson. I certainly had learned one.

Never risk anyone hearing anything personal about the people for whom you are working. Because you know a great deal about them, you will have formed some opinions about the family, and their neighbours or friends. Your opinion is your own, and will undoubtedly change as you get to know them better. Think how distressed you would be to hear your private business discussed on a bus.

So you need an even temperament, and a sense of humour, and the ability to keep confidences about your patients.

We do not need to discuss honesty because it goes without saying. Joe was unwise enough to say to his night carer that she could help herself to anything he kept in the fridge, if she felt hungry in the night. He then was astonished to find she ate him out of just about everything he had, and even drank a bottle of his beer.

Never ever drink alcohol on duty, however persuasively the opportunity presents itself. Never accept the offer of anything but a drink of tea or coffee, or some water. If you are working a long shift, by all means take your meal along, and any special drink you prefer.

Never use any facilities for your own purpose while you are at work. Annette found her carer doing some personal washing while she was there, along with some extra bedding for her patient. Never use those facilities, however friendly you may have become with your patient.

And never accept money, or expensive gifts, from the sick person, or their family. Sometimes after someone has died you may receive a gift as a thank-you for all you did. Make sure your boss knows about it, write a thank-you letter, and keep a copy.

This is not being suspicious about other people. But sometimes in the height of emotional distress, people can do or say things that they may regret later, when everyone is calmer. Paulette, after caring for some weeks for an old lady who lived alone, and who seemed to have a very uncaring family, accepted a lovely brooch from her patient, after the old lady had a terrible night of sickness. Soon, afterwards, she was asked to move to another patient or client, who lived conveniently nearer to Paulette's home. She was shocked to hear from her boss that the old lady was asking for the brooch back, as it had belonged to her mother, and was quite valuable. Paulette was acutely embarrassed at returning it, as she had never asked for it in the first place, and indeed had not wanted to accept it. She realised, too late, that the old lady was using the brooch as a bribe, to keep Paulette there on a permanent basis. When she knew she had left, and had failed in her attempt to keep her, she decided to get the brooch back to try again on another good carer!

Many old people forget and will report something missing that they have actually given away. Be gracious when you refuse a gift. Explain that you are unable to accept anything while you are working. When the job is over, it may be possible to accept a thank-you letter or small gift.

This also applies to a situation that can arise when you may comment on something attractive the patient is wearing, or using. In many cultures, admiring something results in being offered it. Be careful that your enthusiasm does not end up with your refusing a gift, and causing offence or hurt feelings on the part of the giver.

None of this is very hard to understand. But if you are working as a carer, it is a good idea to think about various situations, so that if you come across them you are not caught unaware.

Chapter Four

Empathy

A good carer needs empathy. Empathy is defined by Longman as "the power or state of imagining oneself to be another person, and so of sharing his ideas and feelings". This is not the same as sympathy, and many people who care about others become so sorry for someone, and so embroiled in a situation, that they lose the ability to remain objective. Almost all of us do it at some stage, at least once in a lifetime, whether we are male or female. There are very few people who have spent their life caring in some capacity, who cannot look back and squirm at the over-involvement they can recognise in retrospect.

We need to look at this more closely. If you can see why someone is experiencing certain emotions, and behaving in a certain way, but not become swamped by your own reactions, you can perhaps encourage them to talk through the problem, and be supportive without getting too involved. Of course you must be interested. If you are not interested then do not try to pretend because it is hard to fake an interest for long. But try to remain detached. People sense irritation or lack of understanding, and if you are immediately over-involved and you are very opinionated their response is to become more passionate and less co-operative. They either "close off" emotionally and do not respond, or they shout louder to try and make you understand. Inevitably this leads to friction.

So you have to aim to show a balanced response. Of course you cannot be interested in every detail of a life that is probably quite restricted, and most of the time you can listen and chat without any strain. However there are times when you will, hopefully, be in the position to offer a balanced response to a situation, and be able to help to resolve a problem.

Let us look at an extreme example: James was in hospital following a fall not long after he had been diagnosed with motor neurone disease (MND). He was told he would be discharged into a nursing home as soon as possible. He was forty years old. He had been a fireman for years, and then had been involved in evaluating fire hazard in new buildings. He had never been married, and he had many hobbies and activities that his friends would hopefully continue to help him with, as he became incapacitated. He lived in a top-floor flat, with poor access in that there was only one lift for four residents, and it ended on the floor below James, leaving him about twelve steps to climb. He had lived there for many years. His problems were that he now needed some care with his daily activities, like washing, cooking and cleaning his house. This is now called social care and is not "nursing care", i.e. care from a qualified nurse. But he had been told he might die very quickly indeed, within a matter of months, and he wanted to be at home if that were to be the case. So he might have been offered some palliative care, in the form of monitoring and support, and understanding of his situation. However since he presented with no obvious pain or illness, only an increasing weakness, social services were the only people involved, and they could offer only limited social care.

In the past there was not this problem, since all care came from the same pool of money. Now the budgets are clearly demarcated, and so managers of the services are all watching their balance sheets.

His hospital care team wanted him to go into a home, because they were concerned that in the event of fire in his flat he would be at risk and could die. James, because of his old job, was far more aware of the danger than anyone else was, but he had lived there for many years, and he wanted to die there, if his death was imminent. He did not rate the fire hazard very highly in his present life-threatening situation.

To add to his problems, James was finding his speech was deteriorating, and he often sounded slurred, and drunk, which made any conversation harder to understand. Frustrated by the apparent confusion over what James understood was happening to him, and what help social services were saying he could expect, he became abusive and aggressive and absolutely uncooperative. The overworked and pressurised social services team, tired of trying to make him understand the danger of remaining in his flat, were no longer listening to him. They were concentrating on fighting to get him a temporary place, to release the hospital bed, in the hope that once he was discharged they could perhaps ensure that he stayed put. There was still no mention of support from medical or palliative care services.

After exhausting weeks of arguing, a temporary social worker with some experience of the disease was able to talk with James, and understand, and explain to others why he was so unhelpful. She could have been someone from the MND Association, or anyone from the social services team. By liaising with the other services on offer he was finally able to go home for a trial period, with a package of care that included nursing support, social care and emotional support and monitoring from a hospice team. In fact, he was able never to leave his flat again, as his illness progressed rapidly, as it sometimes does. Also, he decided not to risk any more hospital visits in case he couldn't get out again!!! He was very popular with all his carers, had a devastatingly macabre sense of humour, and led a fulfilling life in his own place until he died.

It took just one person to stand in his shoes long enough to clarify the whole situation.

However, if that person had become over emotionally involved, which would have been easy to do in such sad circumstances, it might have been hard to stand back long enough to explain his viewpoint, in a calm and logical fashion based on the facts.

It is not uncommon for someone like James to find himself in a situation where everyone in the case takes sides, and argues a personal preference, based on personal emotional history. It is so easy to forget that the focal point should be the patient and what he needs to maintain his quality of life in his own home. Unable to speak clearly for himself meant that his needs, as he saw them, could be overlooked by all the services involved in his care.

This was a complicated situation. You may be confronted with something as ordinary as someone wondering whether to make up an argument with a relative or friend. You will need to be objective and not relate the question to your own relationship with a similar relative or friend. If you listen carefully you can begin to see what your patient really wants. If she talks about it, this is because she is concerned about it. The more she talks, to a sympathetic listener, the more she may come to her own conclusions about what to do. Questions like "How would you feel if something happened to her/him?", "Would you regret not having made your peace?", "Is it possible to settle the argument without blaming anyone for the original quarrel?" are about as far as you need to go to help in making decisions.

It is also not always easy to understand what someone else is experiencing. Some things are intensely personal, and as we know our responses to any situation are conditioned by our culture, our upbringing, religion and life experiences. So you must assume that you will not be able to feel empathy immediately, and absolutely, with every person you meet. What you can *always* do is to listen.

Listening is a skill. Listening to someone properly takes great energy and concentration from the listener. So make sure you are comfortable, and are not going to wriggle and fidget. Position yourself so that you are level with the speaker and can offer good eye contact. If the other becomes sidetracked and wanders a bit, try to bring him back to the point, by repeating his last significant remark. Ask a question, if what he says does not seem clear to you. This is especially true when you are hearing something new to you, or different from your own understanding. It does not matter if you think you seem ignorant, the important thing is that you are trying to understand.

Resist the temptation to let your mind wander, and start remembering the next job you have to do, or the letter you haven't posted, or the bill you haven't paid. For this reason you cannot spend hours listening. You may find that ten minutes are the absolute maximum you can manage. So make sure you're clear about how long you have, if this is possible. Sometimes it is not. Time is so expensive nowadays that the job of the carer is almost always made harder by the lack of it.

Alice had heard some terrible news about her family, and in a state of shock she blurted it out to a colleague, Janet, at work. Afterwards she recollected that she had never spoken intimately to Janet before, and never did again. But she felt that she had received more support from

Janet than anyone to whom she told her story. Why was that?

Janet sat quite motionless throughout the story. She kept her eyes on Alice, showing no emotion, and only nodding her head at times. She was not shocked or horrified, but her eyes filled with tears at one point. When Alice had finished, she still said very little, other than she was so sorry it had happened. She didn't offer comfort, or say that time would help, or any of the other platitudes. She didn't try to hug her or make physical contact sensing that Alice was not looking for that. Alice felt a huge lifting of her grief, which although only temporary was a respite for her.

So the art of listening is a huge part of developing empathy, and sometimes words are quite unnecessary, and so are hugs and tears. You will learn to read the person in front of you so that you can give the response that is most helpful to them.

If you listen so closely, you must also be able to leave whatever you have heard behind you when you leave the house. Carers cannot take home with them all the grief and sorrow they gather during the working shift. Listen, empathise, and leave the emotional effects at the door of the house as you go. *Detached compassion* is the best way to describe how to react. If your response is too emotional, the person for whom you are caring will have the added burden of feeling responsible for your peace of mind.

This is a very difficult thing to do. Think about it, and try to make a plan for dealing with the emotions that will be placed on you in the course of your work. You will have experienced friends or family confiding in you at various stages in your life. Try to identify what seemed to help the person confiding in you at that time. You will also have experienced grief and sadness yourself, and if you confided in someone then, try to identify what worked for you, what helped, and what definitely did not.

Since we are talking about listening, and empathy, and talking, we should say that there is one conversation that all carers, whatever their experience, and whatever their qualifications, find very difficult indeed. That is when the invalid, or the family, ask if the patient is going to die. You could think about this question, because at some time, someone will very probably ask you, "Am I going to die?" or "Is she/he going to die?"

Later on we will talk about discussing this with the family when someone is close to dying. However, when someone is apparently feeling fairly well, this question can take everyone by surprise. It is not a question that you can answer easily.

You may have been told that this is a terminally ill person you are caring for. What you cannot do is tell them so. They may have been told that they are not going to get well by the consultant or the oncologist, but you cannot depend on anyone fully accepting this news, and it is not your place to confirm this for them.

It is best to be as honest as you can without being blunt. You could say, "I can't answer your question because I don't know what the doctor has told you. What did the doctor tell you before you left the hospital?" Or, "What makes you ask me that now? Are you feeling really unwell at the moment? Have you asked the doctor what he thinks?"

In other words, help the patient to focus on what has been happening, so he can think about what has already been said to him.

Often the patient asks the question because he has noticed a change in the way his family and friends treat him. If he has not been told the prognosis, he will wonder why everyone is treating him as if he is very ill, when he is expecting to be feeling better. Sometimes the family will ask the consultant not to tell the patient because they themselves cannot cope, or because the patient has often said that they would not want to know if they were ever that ill. If the patient has reason to suspect he is being lied to, it is not uncommon for a person to try to catch you, the carer, out, and trap you into saying more than he has been told.

Peter once asked me this question, because his wife, Amy, was so weepy and frightened all the time. His treatment had left him very weak and he did not feel he was getting any better. There were no carers visiting, and his next appointment was not for several weeks. I suggested gently to him that he should talk to her about his fears when they had a quiet time without visitors. I asked him if I could tell Amy that he had asked me if he was going to die and he agreed. When I told her what he had said, she burst into tears and told me she had been told he could tolerate no further treatment. She couldn't sleep for fear that Peter would be dead when she woke up. I was able to persuade them that they should request an early hospital appointment to review his condition, and then together make a list of questions for their consultant. By doing this they were taking charge of the situation.

The questions were along these lines:

Why no more treatment?
Am I cured then?
If not cured then will I die?
Is there no other treatment?
Don't people die in the hospice?
I/we haven't made a will.

After the hospital appointment they had the following information:

Peter could not have any further treatment without it causing him too much discomfort. His condition was not curable, but the oncologist assured him that he could live

26

with the disease for quite a long time. After all, he had had it for quite a long time without knowing about it. The suggestion was that he would be referred to a palliative care team for symptom control and support. If he had a severe problem, which was unlikely in the near future, he could be admitted to the hospice for a spell. But this was not expected in the near future either. The consultant suggested that they plan for the worst and expect the best. He suggested that that was not a bad attitude to take about life generally! And he suggested they take a holiday and relax after all they had been through over the last months.

Both of them felt better for talking. What they were imagining was far more frightening than anything they had been told.

If patients feel they have some control over what is happening, they will usually manage far more confidently. To enable this to be so, they need to have information from the person who is most informed, which will be the doctor or specialist.

A carer can ask questions to help family members clarify what they are thinking, but a carer cannot tell them what the situation is, even if the carer has been told that the person is terminally ill. You can reassure someone about the role of the hospice, because there are so many myths about hospice care. You can say things like:

"I know it does take a long time to get over some treatments." "If your 'gut feeling' is that you are not getting any better then maybe you should check it out with the specialist."

It may be that a family member can phone or write to the consultant's secretary to ask for a further appointment, but this is the way to get one quickly.

You should never offer uninformed false hope. There is nothing more irritating than to know that something is wrong because you feel ill and depressed and have lost weight as well as other signs, and yet have someone tell you, "You are looking so well. I know everything is okay with you – of course nothing is going to happen to you."

So, spend some time considering how you might deal with such a question. And remember to try and determine from where you will get your support at times of stress, before you meet those times of stress.

Ideally, you should have a supervision period set aside with your team leader, in which you can discuss difficulties. It is rare to find such support. So before you begin this new job, decide on your own way of coping. And remember, if your support is a partner or a friend, they may not have the ability to stay detached, or to keep confidences. Often, carers become so interested in their work that they talk about it all the time. Allow a slot for work discussions, and then keep to it. You must have a life after work.

Chapter Five

Flexibility and adaptability

Carers need to be flexible. This does not mean that you are easily dissuaded from the job in hand, and will stop and chat, or drink tea for ages. It also does not mean that you are set on what you are going to do, and you will do it over all protests. It means that you can appraise a situation, and adapt if necessary. It means that if you are asked to do something at a different time, or in a different fashion, you can decide whether it is possible, without rearranging your life, or that of another member of the team, and if it is, you will do it without complaints.

Some people hate any sort of change. Old people frequently develop a resistance to change even one small part of their lives. They have an inflexible routine, and they like it. They have an unchangeable diet and they like that too. You are not going to make any difference to them whatever you say. Often this is because they have no control anymore over their daily activities, and so they take control when they can. Sometimes they are frightened of change and stay with the routine that seems safe and familiar.

Many sick people feel the same way and for the same reasons. They have very little control in their lives, and so they make the most of what little they can control. Sometimes their confidence in managing their day-to-day life has gone and they stay with what is safe in a changing world. Carers need to understand this.

Some carers go to an extreme when they are caring for someone, and they change every routine to keep the patient happy. But caring is also a partnership, and the carer must have some say in how something is done. We understand that patients have no control over most of their lives, day to day, and they need to feel that they have some say in something. As carers we also know that if the care they get is going to be satisfactory, there must be some continuity and some mutual co-operation. All the carers going into the house must work together, within a timeframe, and therefore they need to know what to do, and what to expect.

Somehow you have to tread a path between what the patient would like, what you have time to do, and what your colleagues coming in after you will expect to find.

Kate was only forty-five years old, recently retired on the grounds of ill health, and she ruled the family with a rod of iron. She played the carers off against each other. All her callers were allocated specified jobs, and were expected to call on time, and with their delegated roles fulfilled. Kate also did her very best to live a life as normal as she had before she became ill. Her chief interest became organising her carers to enable her to do just that. Carers were under constant pressure to fit in with her expectations, and when she saw a weak link she was there in a flash. When Beth, her new carer, arrived she was told that Kate did not fancy her bath as arranged, and she would rather have her hair done. She also hoped Beth could pop round the corner to pick up some things for her. Beth was trying to please, and she followed all instructions. She was tired and had had a long week adapting to this very different work. This was her last call, and the fact that Kate was so young and tragic influenced her too much. She was there for an extra hour, so Kate gave her some tea and lots of flattering compliments about the good care she gave. She left tired, but well satisfied.

Beth's colleague, coming on the following day, was not so pleased when Kate told her she wanted a bath that day. Her working contract was not for a full day, and if she worked over her hours she would not get paid overtime. She was supposed to give Kate a wash, and get her dressed. When she pointed this out, she received a stream of abuse, along with some very unkind comparisons to Beth, which both hurt and offended her.

Beth was upset to have started a new job and almost immediately caused much animosity from her new team mates. Kate demanded of the team managers that Beth come on a regular basis, and more frequently than she was able. Even Beth began to see that Kate had a problem with control, and would not be an easy patient if she did not have her way.

The team should have given her some better information. The situation took a while to resolve, and Beth stopped being Kate's favourite carer, and soon was receiving the same amount of criticism as the others.

We will be talking about records later in the book, but it is a good idea to keep your own record of the person you visit, what you do, and how long you are there. This does not have to be an essay – just a few careful jottings just after you leave the house. Community workers of all categories usually keep such a record, for their personal use, as well as the home records they have to maintain, which can be legally requested by the courts if there is a claim against the services or an individual.

Jill found her records a great help when, several years after she started another job, she was asked by a solicitor to confirm a conversation with a patient about his will.

Following the death of the man, his daughter found she had been excluded from a last-minute will, in favour of a very distant family member, who had been with the ill man in the last few days of his life, when he was fast deteriorating mentally.

Jill had a record of her conversation with him, regarding his daughter, which, although brief, made it clear that when he was in his right mind he had no intention that anyone, other than his much-loved daughter, should inherit his money and house.

You may never have a similar experience, but keeping a short record for your own interest is a very useful and professional way to work. Long after you have finished work, your records may be a source of interest to you, and others, and a reminder of your experiences.

Adaptability

Carers need to be adaptable. When you are going into the homes of strangers, you need to be able to adapt to their way of doing something, while maintaining a recognisable standard that someone following you can immediately recognise. This means you have to look at the way you work, in every aspect. Unless you are asked to do something that you consider absolutely out of order, you are the one who must make the effort. You are a guest in the home of a sick person, with all the stress that this implies. We will discuss things you cannot agree to in more detail later on.

Carers sometimes have a problem with patients asking them to collect some shopping for them on their way to their work. This may be something your employers have rules about, but if not, you must decide what you can do in the time allotted to a patient. You may feel able to pick up small items on your way, but from the start you will be wise to make clear the amount of shopping you are able to do. You will not want to arrive every day weighed down with several bags. So be very clear. "I am happy to collect light shopping for you, Mrs Brown, but I have my own bags to carry, and cannot manage anything heavy." And whatever you buy, present the receipt to your patient, and collect the money, making sure that you check it properly with a third person if you can.

Sometimes people have demands or requests that seem unreasonable or unnecessary to you. Try to put yourself in their place and comply with what they want if you can. Lola had a very sick husband, and she knew he would not live to be old. They had a nice house in the middle of the city, and she was very house proud. Anyone who came into her home was expected to remove outdoor shoes to protect the floor. She had a lot of arguments with the carers. One in particular never removed her shoes because she said she had not the time. (In private she felt that Lola was ridiculous and that she needed to be taught a lesson!!) Another never cleared anything away. She left damp towels, wash cloths, wash bowls, and dirty plates all around. (She said she had not got time to clear up.) Lola became more and more irritated with each day that passed. Any benefit the family might have got from the visit was buried in the general animosity.

The carer left for another patient. The new carer to join the team of six regulars, all working in rotation, started the following morning. Let us call her Jo. Jo arrived on time and introduced herself with a big friendly smile. When asked rather abruptly to remove her shoes she immediately did so. She took a few moments to read the notes about Lola's husband Gavin. She explained what she was going to do and worked with an ongoing commentary from Lola, who became less wary as the time passed. Jo spent an extra few minutes just explaining how she worked, what she would attempt to get done, and how she was placed for the rest of the day.

In less than a week, Jo had the whole situation running smoothly. Because she always cleared up after herself, and tried to leave the place neat, Lola was quick to offer to clear up when Jo was a bit pushed for time. Jo made Gavin laugh, teased him gently, and treated him respectfully at the same time. She worked more quickly than her predecessor, but it was her attitude that made all the difference. Her colleagues noticed the change at once, because when she left the atmosphere was lighter, and this lasted most of the day. As a carer, remember that you may be one of the few people who go to that house to do something practical. Your manner, your mood and your attitude to your job will affect the household all day, long after you have finished your shift and gone home. That may carry over to the next person coming into the house, so another carer following your shift may have a difficult time as well. Jo did all the small extra jobs willingly, but was also able to say "I can't do that today, but I will do it tomorrow if there's time after we change the sheets." She understood Lola's need to keep the house in order. After all she had to be in it all day with many visitors, lots of often frustrating phone calls, equipment everywhere, and very little free time to call her own.

The other point of this story is to emphasise that as a visitor you can affect the mood for the whole day for the patient and the family. In turn this affects all the other callers, whether they come for a moment or for an hour, socially or professionally.

This may sound very difficult, but please do not feel discouraged. You may also feel that you would deal with some of the situations differently. This is not a blueprint for managing situations – just some ideas and examples to consider.

If you do make a mistake, and realise in time that you

could have handled a situation differently, you only have to say something like: "I am sorry, that was a bad start. I understand what you are saying, so can we try again and see if I can do better this time."

Most people will respond to an apology and, even if you feel it was not all your fault, you are going to be on your way very soon. The patient will be left to fume for what may be hours. Make your peace and you will also feel better.

Chapter Six

Negotiating skills

Negotiating skills are useful in many areas of life, but particularly when you are working in someone's personal space. There are some regular grumbles about carers that we can try to anticipate, and maybe lessen or avoid the irritation for those concerned.

Carers usually have one common problem from the very beginning. You as the professional carer will have a case list of several people to see in the course of a day. All of them will, almost definitely, want you to come at the same time, either between 8 to 9 a.m., which is when they want to get up, or 8 to 10 p.m., when they will want to go to bed. They are trying to keep as normal a life as possible, and a normal life for them has rarely included getting up at 11.30 a.m., and going to bed at 7 p.m. They will see you as being difficult if you cannot oblige. There are few people who are relaxed enough to be prepared to step down and be inconvenienced for another person, whom the carer considers has a greater need.

You have to plan your visit according to the needs of the patients, and also the demands of distance and time. You cannot run up huge mileage costs, nor waste time crisscrossing long distances between cases, and neither can you call on the heaviest and lengthiest case first, which will mean your second call may be after lunch.

Likewise, you have a list of jobs to do in a certain order. Maybe you will wash or bath someone, or maybe just hastily help with getting dressed. You have an allocated time to spend with people, and you are not paid overtime. If you allow yourself to get sidetracked, you end up working far more hours than you are paid to do. Now, not only are you not covered by your employer's insurance to work at those times, but you are laying up troubles for all the carers who come after you. And that is not to mention the fact that you will never manage your timetable and will always be running late. It is all too easy to end up with no life at all, apart from work.

You will need all your skills to keep everyone happy with the time you have allocated to each task.

It is not so very different in an institution or a hospital. You still have a routine to keep to, and other people to consider in the course of the day.

It is not easy to keep a balance that will satisfy all the parties concerned. And most of us fail dismally, at some stage or another. I did early on in my career, when the demands of the job swamped me emotionally. My colleagues must have been very frustrated. It is a shame that none of them sat down with me and tried to discover why I was so driven. In fact, it was a combination of lack of money and personal problems, which did not disappear in the weight of the job, but about which I could avoid thinking, if I worked long and hard enough. Naturally the patients loved the 100 per cent and more I could and often did give them, but what about people who followed me, and could not work in such an over-involved way? Sick people can be very manipulative, because they often need to be, and if you are needy yourself they will be able to squeeze more out of you.

You are a team, and should give each other the kind of support and care that you would each like to receive for yourself.

Giving support is not the same as acting as a prop for someone who cannot manage the work. It is not easy to confront friends or colleagues who are not pulling their weight as part of the team. The worst way of coping is to mutter behind the back of the person at fault. There are times when we all need a friend to "cover" for us when we have an unexpected problem. Some people have more than their fair share of problems, and will require more than an occasional "helping hand". How can you anticipate beforehand that helping out may begin to become a habit, and that you'll start to feel used by someone?

There really is not an easy answer. If you are being regularly asked to stand in for someone, ask yourself a few questions.

> What kind of reasons does this person give for failing to meet her commitments? Does she respond to other people who have a problem, or is she always too busy and too self-absorbed?

If you feel that you are beginning to get irritated by constantly helping out, then say so. Do not talk behind the person's back. This can only too easily become a kind of persecution, and can lead to isolation and misery for the one involved. Groups often do this. Decide that you will not join in.

Ask the person concerned for a private word, and then be firm and clear about what you want to say. Keep a low voice and do not accuse. For example:

> "I have to talk to you about the way I feel about work at the moment. Every time you follow me

on a shift, you are at least ten minutes late. This means that I miss my bus and I am an hour later getting home. I know you have family, and so do I, and it's hard to fit everything in, but I would like it if you could make an effort to arrive on time, so that I can leave on time. Is it a problem for you to get to work by that time?"

"I am quite happy to give you a lift to work, but if you are late, it makes me late as well, and looks bad on my record. Can you please be outside ready for me so that I do not have to wait in future?"

"Can we talk about Mrs—? I know she is a complicated case but can I explain to you why I have a problem following on from your shift with her?"

If the problem is that the place is a mess when you arrive, it may be that your colleague has too much to do before she leaves. You need to talk it over amicably, so that you both know how you feel. It is very unsatisfying to walk into a really messy house to start a shift, and it is also frustrating to have to leave a mess for a colleague. You may well find that you both have a point to make.

It is no different when you work in a unit or ward and have set shifts. It is often easy to get into bad habits when you are working with several colleagues, equally easy to let resentments build up. If possible always try to talk the problem through.

Only if you have made all attempts to co-operate and failed should you take the problem to your manager.

Peggy was an untidy worker. She lived in perpetual chaos, and her colleagues all dreaded following her in a case, because they usually had to clear up after her, and often pacify the patient, before they could start on their own work. She had been involved in many quarrels with team mates, and the problem seemed impossible to resolve until Sara negotiated a plan that Peggy would work for three weeks with her as a partner. She literally trained Peggy in that time. Peggy had grown up in chaos, and simply had no idea of how messy she was. She lived in her house in the same way. A large part of her life was spent trying to undo the muddle she lived in. She had no idea of how to plan a routine and follow it. She was kind-hearted and willing, but she had no idea how to start. From being frustrated to a point of screaming, Sara had a sudden insight into how hard it was for Peggy to manage her day. She began to feel considerable sympathy for her, because working in such chaos left her always late, and always tired, and dissatisfied with her job. Once Peggy began to comprehend the idea of planning, she learned quickly, and enjoyed her work more. But Sara had the right approach because, instead of criticising and sniping at her, she supported her, and made the learning fun.

Unfortunately managers often do not have the funding to apply this kind of logical help, and so would rather lose than improve a carer. You may find it hard to get the management support, and that will require even better negotiating skills.

When negotiating with management, the same principles apply. State your case firmly, without bringing personalities into the discussion, and arguing defensively. If you think you are not being dealt with in a just manner, ask for an appointment, and state your case firmly and quietly. Do not be drawn into long arguments involving personalities. Always keep a record of what was said, and where, and when. Never let a meeting develop into a shouting match. And never make threats of leaving for another job, unless you are prepared to carry them out.

Unions are sometimes poorly thought of now, and certainly the behaviour of some union members has been less than exemplary, but we should remember that working conditions for the average man, before there were unions, were pretty horrendous.

There is also the question of legal protection in case of accident or injury. Personally I would not work in any of the caring professions without having legal cover. Not only do you need protection for your patients, you may need it for yourself at some point. Your employer will cover you for some accidents, but you need to clarify the conditions. Before you start work, look at the contract, talk to colleagues, and apply to several unions for information. There are many workplaces that have a "no union" policy, and it is a good idea to ask about this if you have the opportunity. However, in most situations, you should be able to negotiate your problems yourself, without resorting to union action. It is only in the last resort that you may need to consult your union for action rather than advice.

Sometimes there is no way you can negotiate with someone, and then you have the choice of leaving the job or putting up with unsatisfactory conditions. This is not a failure on your part if you have genuinely tried to make it work. Decide what you will do and get on with it, and learn from the experience. Do not let it dominate your life for any length of time.

It is also true that no situation is ever static for long. Margaret worked in a care home where many of the staff had been in place for years. They had become lazy and uninterested, and usually left the new staff to do all the work, finding endless ways to bully new carers, avoid any real work, and leave shifts early. She tried different ways of coping but finally found the job too much for her and applied for another one within the same company. She quickly settled in and was happy in the work again.

Maureen had a similar situation, was reluctant to move and hung on in the job, managing as best she could. She found that within a year some of the most uninterested members of staff had left, some were off sick, some changed when they were forced to break up their cliques and work alongside someone else. It seemed that huge changes took place almost unnoticed and she suddenly found she began to enjoy her work more and more.

If you are really unhappy you will need courage to make a stand. If you really feel you are justified in being critical, take your time, consider your approach, and decide on your action and then stick to it. Working in the homes of sick people can be so rewarding and enjoyable but it is also very hard work, and if you are unhappy you will quickly become depressed and demotivated. This is not good for you or anyone you meet in the course of the job.

Chapter Seven

Punctuality

Carers need to be good timekeepers, as we have already seen. This is important wherever you work, but particularly important when you are working in the home of a sick person. Part of your skill is the ability to be punctual. This is difficult and often impossible when you travel by public transport or in the cities. If you are going to be late, phone and say so and explain. Even if you are working in a ward, you should be sure to inform your colleagues if you are held up.

In their own homes, you may find that patients will be able to fill in the time by doing something helpful for you, and if not, at least they will not have to sit and wait for you, while constantly watching the clock. Of course they will still be waiting, but with much less anxiety. As we all know, it is increasingly difficult to arrive on time in many large cities, because of traffic congestion, and poor public transport. Most people know this and usually they understand, but they need reassurance that you will come eventually. Many become very anxious if they think they may have been forgotten, or if they think you will not be able to give them the time you have allocated.

Arriving on time not only increases the family confidence in you, but it also helps the family to improve *its* own timekeeping. It is so hard to keep to a schedule when you are a full-time carer, looking after a house, and maybe a family, as well as someone who is sick or incapacitated. Very few people have any insight into the problems, though you, as a carer calling regularly, will be more aware than most. Trying to keep a routine means that plans can be made, instead of only taking each day at a time, and living in a constant state of catching up. When you are a full-time carer, there is often a desperate need to take time off for a hairdo, or shopping trip, or just escape from the sick room for a coffee with friends. When you think about it, you can understand how desperate your patient and their family may become.

In many ways your caring encompasses the entire household. Caring is a job that is, and should be, more than washing a person, or changing a bed.

Caring means looking at the whole picture, and noticing when the situation seems likely to collapse. So your time is very precious to everyone in your environment. You must keep a private life for yourself as well as doing this very important work. You may find that the people you visit have no interest in your personal life, and no sympathy if you are delayed and running late. This is often a response the family have learned, because so many people come and go, without informing the family of any changes in the timetable. However when they become used to your excellent communication and care, most will quickly become more aware of you as a person, and will usually want to co-operate.

What about the people who will always have a last-minute request, designed to keep you just that extra five minutes? Sometimes these people are just very good at delaying tactics. With experience you may learn to recognise the person who simply does not want to be left alone, because they are scared and lonely. Or perhaps someone cannot quite pluck up the courage to tell you something very important. It is so frustrating to have to cut someone short and leave, and it is also very distressing for the patient.

One way to deal with this situation is to say clearly when you arrive how long you can stay, and what the time is when you arrive, and when you will be leaving. You can do this very pleasantly.

> "Hello, Mrs Brown. It's ten o'clock so I am in good time today for you to have a nice wash. I will be leaving at eleven so I'll start getting you up now, so I don't have to hurry you."

> "Hello, Mrs Brown, I am so sorry I am a bit late. Let's see, today was a short visit anyway, so what can I do to make it useful for you? I can stay till eleven so what is the most useful thing I can do while I am here?"

There will still be people who start a very intimate conversation, just as you try to close the door. You may have to be very frank.

> "I wish I could stay and talk about this today, Mrs Brown, but I really have to go now. I know it is important to you, so when I arrive tomorrow can I remind you of where we are, so we can start where we are leaving off today?"

This is not an ideal response, and there will be times when you feel very inadequate, and many times when you feel it is almost impossible to do this. Certainly it is impossible sometimes, for example if someone is suicidal, or in a state of collapse, you cannot just leave them, but this is a rare occurrence fortunately. What is important to remember is that when you arrive the next time, you must remember to remind your patient/client, so that he/she has the opportunity to continue, and also can see that you were interested, and you do want to listen. And you can only hope that the conversation can pick up where it left off.

Again I would emphasise that it is a very good idea to keep a record for yourself. Then if you say you will bring a book, or do a favour for someone in the family, or just that you will have time for a cup of tea, you can remind yourself and *do* it.

The agency that employs you should have some guidelines for the way you work. Make sure you understand what you are expected to do, and then make sure the patient also knows what you are expected, and expecting, to do. If there is a discrepancy, then bring it up as soon as you learn of it. And if you feel that there is no time to complete the tasks set for you, make sure you state that clearly as soon as possible.

Carers cost the country a lot of money, though they save the country even more, and the people who are paying you want to know that you are providing a good service. You are not making trouble if you act to improve the service, and if you are never given enough time to do a proper job the service will need improving.

What about the times when your boss asks you to work on without lunch, and well past the time you are due to finish? This has to be your decision, but you could bear one or two facts in mind.

You need proper rest, food and fluids when you are working in a stressful situation. You have to look after yourself, and you should expect support from your colleagues and managers. Sharon felt responsible for the people she could not care for, because she had too big a caseload. So she worked on, later and later every day. She lost weight, and had problems fitting in any activities other than work. Her colleagues frankly used her to do the jobs that others didn't want to do. Patients who were initially grateful for her commitment began to weary of her late, rushed visits, and her rather more frequent whining about her lot. Finally she strained her back, and was off sick. Her boss was suddenly moved on, and her new boss was not sympathetic when her initial back problem developed into stress, then depression. This all too often happens when you suddenly get relief from a stressful situation, and have time to appreciate just how bad the situation has become, and realise that you do not want to do it anymore.

The lack of sympathy was the last straw, and Sharon left her job completely, feeling much abused. The service lost a very good and responsible carer, who might have gone on and done her NVQ exams, and made a career of caring. She took a long time to recover her spirits, and lost a lot of confidence in her ability to work.

Joan was quite the opposite, and when asked to do extra visits she looked at her clock, and asked why her workload had suddenly increased. The boss explained that someone had had an accident, and Joan agreed to work on this one occasion for an extra hour, but made it clear that she was not prepared to do this on a regular basis. When it happened a few days later she refused. She was then accused of being uncooperative. She immediately rallied her colleagues and they made a joint written complaint about the extra visits they were expected to do at short notice. The matter was resolved by the agency examining the facts, accepting that it needed a spare relief carer to step in at short notice. While the matter was in dispute, there was bad feeling between all the staff, but when it was resolved, everyone benefited. Their employers had to accept that a good service could only increase their profits in the long run. Complaining customers can spread the word very quickly and can damage reputations all too soon.

Punctuality can be seen as an indication of reliability in the eyes of the clients or patients as well as the managers. You will not be considered difficult if you are known to be reliable, and your mobile phone is a great asset in giving this kind of reassurance to the people you work with and for.

The other point to this story is that there are rules about lifting and handling heavy people. In fact lifting is not in the vocabulary of the carer or her employers. The regulations mean that the weight you move must be assessed, and aids put in homes where there are heavy people to move. This means that you are responsible for caring for your own back, and, if all the precautions are not followed and you are injured, it is your responsibility, and you have no support from your managers. A bad back can last a lifetime and cause pain for years. It is not a sensible risk to run. If there is a hoist in a house you must use it, and if there is not and you feel there should be, then you must request an assessment immediately.

Unfortunately most people hate having a hoist used on them. Older people feel very vulnerable, as does anyone who has difficulty moving, seeing properly, or hearing what is being said. Many people will not have been able to get into a bath, perhaps for a very long time, for example, and the experience of being lifted and swung in the air, and then lowered into a bath, can be very scary. Often this is because the carer has not had adequate training, because most hoists are very efficient once the carer has learned how to use them. I once worked in a unit where the nurses practised using hoists and wheelchairs on each other, and I realised that you do not have to be old and infirm to be very nervous when being moved by these means. Make sure you are confident in using any appliances wherever you work, and take your time to explain to your patient the need for the equipment, and your ability to use it safely.

Read your conditions of service, and talk to a union representative if you feel you are not getting the support you need to do the job.

Chapter Eight

Familiarity

What do we mean by familiarity? If you have someone coming to your door to do a job in your home, whom you have never met before, and he walks straight in, and pushes past you, saying "Hello, Jane. Where's the damage? I've only got a moment," you might find that you immediately feel less than friendly. If he calls you Mrs—, and explains who he is, and why he is there, it will not take him longer, and you may well end up on first-name terms in a short while anyway.

If you are seventy-plus years old, living alone and not feeling too well, and are perhaps a little deaf or short-sighted, and, most likely, feeling extremely apprehensive about a carer coming for the first time, the chances are that you will be intimidated by such an approach, or at the very least irritated.

Try to put yourself in the shoes of the person for whom you are caring, and the family.

When you arrive at a new client's, always introduce yourself, and if necessary spell your name, and then repeat it again. And always remember that a smile works wonders at breaking down barriers. Then ask the patient, "What do you like to be called? Is it okay if I call you that?" While many people are happy with the use of Christian names, and it is common practice nowadays in all walks of life, many elderly, and even not-so-elderly people, appreciate you asking them first. When they tell you, make sure you use the name several times to check the pronunciation, and also to help to remember it. And give your full name clearly, and specify the name or version you prefer. For example, "My name is Elizabeth, but I would rather you call me Liz."

Many older patients actually like to call the carer by a title of sorts. They seem to feel more confident, reminding themselves of your role, especially when you are doing very personal care for them. Children also may often call you Nurse. And as a carer you are nursing, but you are not qualified as a nurse. So make sure that you establish the name that makes everyone feels comfortable, and leaves everyone aware of your role. It was easier years ago when we had enrolled nurses who were called "Nurse", and were often the ones who gave really excellent "hands-on" care.

Not unrelated to this point is the question of interest in someone as opposed to being seen as nosy. When you have established a relationship with someone, it is easy to ask personal questions: if they have ever been married, what kind of work they did, how they got on with their mother. As friendships develop, people exchange information, at all levels, quite easily. You would not dream of accosting a stranger with "Hello, isn't it a nice day, and how do you get on with your mother-in-law then?" You would be regarded as a nosy parker at the very least. At worst you may get quite an aggressive response. And yet many people, working in the home of a virtual stranger, ask very intrusive and personal questions without thinking. Once you have established a relationship the question may be viewed quite differently.

Because a person who is bedridden or housebound may

feel he has little to talk about, it can be difficult to establish a conversation. So, asking questions is the obvious way to learn about someone and see what you have in common, and build some kind of relationship. Questions about his family or his interests have to be asked gently and with genuine interest. Take your time to establish a bond, and give information back about your own life in small doses so the patient does not feel it an inquisition. Many old and young people have fascinating stories to tell, and they love to tell them, and if you are washing them or performing personal care, the time passes quickly and much more enjoyably. Sick people have to answer so many questions, repetitive and intrusive, that they often respond eagerly to questions asked with genuine interest, which may also uncover lost or forgotten happy memories.

We have already said that carers should make a real effort to smell clean and fresh. This may sound obvious, but let us think about this for a moment. When you have been working all day, you will inevitably become hot and sticky at times. A good deodorant is essential. Never use perfume to freshen up. Perfume is very individual. People who are ill have often very sensitive noses. And a strong smell can nauseate a sick person, or irritate the lungs of someone who has been experiencing chemotherapy, or has breathing difficulties, due to infection or disease. Keep your perfumes for when you are not at work. The same applies to other strong smells. Garlic is usually a complete turn-off if someone is close to you on a bus – so don't take a chance on really causing discomfort to your patients. If you smoke a quick cigarette in the back garden or the street just before you arrive, the smell of tobacco can be overwhelming to someone who does not share that habit. A good tip to remember is that eating parsley is an excellent deodorant. It removes smells far more effectively than a spray of peppermint. (This is a good tip for your patients who get embarrassed by odours, particularly when they have a colostomy bag. Tell them to try adding a regular spoonful of parsley to their food during the day. It is also a good source of iron.)

You do not have to deprive yourself of your pleasures – it is just a question of being aware of the sensitivities of the person you are there to care for. Everyone at some time has been close to someone who is wearing a perfume that we find unpleasant or overpowering, or who has a strong stale body odour, either on the person or on her clothes. If you had to stay around that person for several hours, and then endure the smell lingering in your own home, when she leaves, you might find it quite unbearable. And if you are in a ward, or have a room in a residential home, you might have several carers, and if they all wear strong perfume, or have a strong body odour, the room could have a heavy residual smell.

Sometimes visiting carers want to change things, to make their work easier for them. If your job is hampered by the furniture layout, or lack of facilities, and a small change can make a difference, talk to your patient and explain what you would like to do, and why. But remember, you are a guest in someone's home, so do not force a change that will upset the patient, especially when he will have to lie there all day, and brood over something over which he has no control.

Again, this begins to sound as if you have to be an angel, and a vision of perfection. Let me reassure you. This is not the case. None of us is perfect. But if you are really making an effort to do the very best you can, for the people for whom you are caring, you will enjoy the work more, and the appreciation you receive will spur you on.

This is harder to do now than ever before, because the time you spend at work is so closely monitored. Time is money, in the world of the carer, and especially the carer working in the community. Of course this has always been the case, and I am sure that in the past some people have been guilty of wasting time on their home visits. But in my experience the timewasters are few and far between, because there is always more to do than you have time for. However, it means that it can be difficult to assess and record the value of time spent with a patient, because a few moments extra can give you a greater insight into the general situation, and that can sometimes avert a potential problem. If you do not learn to do this, you may never know what you have missed. But it takes time. Making a strong bond of trust cannot be achieved in seconds with someone who is deeply distressed and frightened or angry, who may also have a history of short, unsatisfactory interaction with a series of specialists, all limited by time and large caseloads. Years ago the community nurse and the general practitioner were able to support families through many troubles that are now referred to specialist nurses, psychiatric nurses, and various other professionals. This is not to say that the way it happens now is not as effective, but I believe it does sometimes mean that there is a greater chance of signs and symptoms being missed at a very early stage.

So, the carer needs to monitor her skills in communication, and develop a way of working that offers the patient assurance of receiving good care, so that trust can develop in the relationship. Working in an organised fashion means that you do not seem to be in a hurry all the time, which is a terrible deterrent when you are trying to build a relationship.

One of the single commonest causes of complaint arises when the visiting carer needs help and comes with a colleague. Margaret Forster recalls this memorably in her book *Precious Lives*, where she describes a visit by the night nurses to her much-loved sister-in-law, as she neared the end of her life. She describes the way she heard the nurses arrive, by the loud laughter outside the door, and how they barged in, and clattered up the stairs, talking about "doing the patient". Margaret tells how the two nurses managed to spoil the atmosphere of calm and peace completely, which had prevailed in the house until their arrival, and she cancelled the service after only one or two visits. Like so many other people, in a time of stress, she did not complain, or give a reason for the cancellation. She simply wanted them out, and not to see them again. And so those two nurses will continue to work in such an unprofessional way, and will continue to cause grief to families, who often feel they have in some way "let down" the sick person by permitting the nurses to behave in such a fashion.

Margaret's immensely readable book has identified a crucial problem of attitude that is sadly prevalent in hospitals as well. If you can imagine your mother, or sister, or your son, ill and frightened, being heaved around by two strangers, who talk loudly over their head, and make no attempt to tell the patient what they will do next, you can begin to get the idea.

Most people have observed this attitude in hospital, either with a loved one, or when they are visiting someone. When screens are around a bed, it is easy to think you are invisible. If you cannot always imagine that the person you are caring for is someone's mother, father, husband, wife or child, then try to think of a watcher, who can see every move and hear all you say. Keep your private conversation for your tea breaks, or for when you are off duty.

Whether alone or with a colleague, in the home of a sick person, or in a hospital or nursing-home environment, when you are handling a patient, talk quietly and clearly to her, even if she appears to be quite unconscious. Tell her what you are going to do, and how you are going to move her. You do not need to talk constantly; you can work in silence too. Just be yourself, and if you are comfortable with talking and not getting a response, it can be very good for focusing your mind on what you are doing. For example you might say, "Hello, Mary. I am Sue, and this is Jane, and we are going to change your bed, and give you a little wash. I shall start by taking some of your covers off like this, but don't worry, we won't let you catch cold."

Always remember, however that person appears now, she was once just like you, and one day you may be just like her. She may be very well aware of all you say and do, but just not able to reply to you.

Penny was a nurse. She worked all her life in one hospital, until she became a sister, in charge of the ward. She ran the ward smoothly and efficiently, but she had no personal warmth, and never attracted personal confidences from either staff, visitors, or patients. When she was in her early fifties, she became ill with multiple sclerosis. She found her change of role unbearable, and as her illness progressed she seemed to give in completely, and just wanted to die. In one of the last conversations she had with a district nurse she said that she felt her life had been a complete waste, and she wished she could turn back the clock, and once again have the chance to meet all those hundreds of people for whom she had cared, and to whom she had given nothing of herself. She tried to tell everyone who visited about her regrets, and perhaps one or two heard her and tried to comfort her, but in the end she died lonely and sad. However, her last words echoed among her colleagues, and over time made many of them thoughtful enough to try to find a different way of working.

You may think that you are talking just for the benefit of the family, and if that were the case it would still be completely justified. In fact people who work in intensive care units with unconscious patients, and people who work with the dying, all say with conviction that hearing is the last sense we lose. There are hundreds of examples of people very close to death, who can respond in tiny ways, to show that they have heard what has been said. And many examples of people who, on recovering from such a state, can confirm that they heard every word.

It is also very obvious to any observer when someone has been handled with love and gentleness. The patient will not be restless, the family will not feel they need to be around to protect the patient, and everyone will be calm and trusting when the next carers come in turn. For you as the carer, seeing that result will more than outweigh the effort you put into the job.

Chapter Nine

Coping with aggression

Unfortunately, it is becoming more common for carers to face aggression, in the form of verbal abuse, and even the threat of physical abuse.

You should have guidelines from your manager so be sure you read them carefully. There are also some things you can do to protect yourself, and some signs to watch for, to anticipate problems.

If you are anxious about someone and feel threatened, do not wait until the situation becomes frightening. Make sure there is no barrier between you and the exit, clarify the situation and, if necessary, take steps to get out of the area. If, and this is not so likely, you really feel that someone is going to harm you, leave *immediately* if it is at all possible, and report the situation to your manager. If someone is verbally or racially abusive, or sexually harasses you, you do not have to tolerate that behaviour. Do not panic, stay calm and leave quietly.

The first rule of visiting in the community is to make sure that someone knows where you are. Anyone making house calls without leaving a record of where she will be going in the course of the day is taking a risk. It takes a moment to note, in a diary, the expected order of your visits. You will have already decided where you are going, and your manager or administrator should know as well. But always leave a record for your family in your own home, just in case.

Most people carry a mobile phone, and this is one career in which a phone is invaluable.

At the very least, always carry in your car a small kit containing maps, pens, snacks and a notebook with handy numbers in it, and a small sum of money, especially if you do not have a mobile phone.

Always make sure that you have enough petrol, and your car is maintained well, if you are not using public transport.

If you *are* using public transport, make sure you have a bag with maps, some money, a snack, and essential phone numbers.

As we discussed in an earlier chapter, keep a record of the time you arrive and leave, jotted down in your notebook.

On arrival, and after introducing yourself, take a moment to check out your feelings about the place and the patient.

Many elderly people can appear brusque and quite aggressive, because they are confused and frightened. You need to observe the whole situation, the attitude of anyone else present, and the condition of the person who is making you uneasy.

Does he sound confused? How able would he be if he tried to carry out a threat?

Never underestimate old people, however frail they may appear. Jill was working in a geriatric unit as an agency nurse. She knew quite a few patients and staff, and was familiar with the layout of the building, and felt quite confident about working there at night. One evening, she was walking up some stairs and she met an old man coming down, whom she vaguely recognised. She gave him a bright "Good evening" and was a bit surprised to be kicked in the stomach. Even with bedroom slippers on his feet, he packed enough of a punch to send her to the bottom of the stairs, whereupon he followed her and kicked her twice more, before scurrying off up the corridor. When she finally found help, the old man had already been recaptured, and was back in bed. He was confused, and although considered too weak to walk without help, he had climbed out of bed, and tried to escape. When he met someone in a uniform, he was afraid she would recapture him, so he attacked.

When she later did her rounds, and saw him sitting in bed, she stopped and again said "Good evening," and she was told, "Well it is good now you have come, but I have had a terrible day today." He had no memory of kicking her downstairs the first time he saw her.

So, never underestimate old people. If they are frightened and desperate, they can be very strong and violent. We may be the same in similar circumstances.

Resist the temptation to shout back or argue. This can only exacerbate the situation. Always keep your voice down, and speak calmly and clearly. Repeat the same thing several times. Do not interrupt, and never make a physical move that could be seen as threatening. Remember that your patient is ill, and may not really understand what is happening, or may have a completely different perspective on the situation. Whatever happens, respond immediately if there seems to be a move to settle the argument, and make peace.

When working as a specialist nurse, I was asked to see a man who had undergone surgery for bowel cancer. He was in his mid-forties, and the surgery had come as a great shock to him. He was being cared for in a small local hospital, where specialist nurses were only able to visit once a week or so. He could not manage his colostomy bag, and in the busy ward no one had the time to show him properly. He had no proper equipment, no time to get used to the idea of surgery, and he was fuming with life in general. When I approached him and introduced myself, he flew at me shouting, "Where the **** have you been? What the **** are you being paid for? If I did my job like you do yours I would be fired." There were similar remarks, all yelled out at the top of his voice, in the main general ward. I was too surprised to speak, and sat in complete silence for a moment. Then I said, as sympathetically as I could through my nervousness and irritation, that I could see he was extremely angry, and that I was very sorry to have been so long in coming. To my further surprise, he then burst into tears.

He improved rapidly after his ordeal, and it was only months later, when he was at home and doing well, that I was able to tell him that on that initial visit I had seen him only by accident, due to a series of blunders in professional communication. He was in fact a charming and friendly person, but I could not have guessed that from our first encounter.

If the aggression is coming from a relative of someone else in the house then you have a different problem. You must make it clear that you do not have to stay in a place where you are feeling threatened. Again most people are anxious and worried, and if they are not under the influence of drink or drugs, they are most likely to calm down if your response is firm but also reassuring.

If there are drugs involved, or if someone is drunk, then you must judge for yourself whether you feel at risk, and act accordingly. You do not have to work in such an environment. But make the decision based on your safety, and not your moral judgement.

Never forget that the people you are working for are ill, or helpless in some way, which means that they are probably very frustrated. You do not know what has happened in their day to exacerbate the frustrations they are experiencing.

If they are cornered, and feel attacked, or bullied, they may respond in what would be a wholly unusual way for them. Do all you can to prevent them from getting angrier and acting out their aggression, because once they have passed the point of no return and attacked physically, it will be very hard to regain control of the situation.

Most important of all, be sure that you keep your escape route clear, and, if you are not certain, ask for someone to accompany you for one or two visits, while you clarify your impressions.

This does not mean that this is a dangerous job, and you must always be on your guard. It does mean that you must stay "aware" rather than "on alert", and keep a record of where you are, and an idea of the times you keep.

Chapter Ten

Setting boundaries

Boundaries are especially important when you are caring for someone for a long time, either as a live-in carer or for long shifts at a time on a regular basis. We have already talked about some of these issues in the chapter on familiarity. Some parts of this chapter may also be relevant to carers working in a hospital or nursing home. It is easy to rummage through a drawer, or handbag, forgetting that this may be the only place someone has to keep private letters, or photos, or even money, when they are hospitalised.

If you are living in the house of a patient, you must set some clear rules to maintain your privacy and theirs.

You need a room of your own that is private. If it is possible for you to have your own fridge, and it is offered, that is very useful. If not, you must keep your food clearly marked, and make sure that you use only yours. Many people will tell you to help yourself to anything you need. However this often leads to misunderstandings, and you need to clarify exactly what is meant by "help yourself".

Mrs Gray was very hospitable when she employed Katy as a full-time carer. She had never had someone living in before, and wanted to make her feel at home. Katy felt very fortunate, and made herself very much at home, eating her way through the food in the fridge, and a bottle of wine that was also cooling there. She soon began to stay up late, and invited friends, who were noisy, and cooked meals there. She also made many telephone calls. Mrs Gray survived all this, without complaining, but the relationship between them broke down after Katy had a boyfriend there for the weekend.

So here are a few DOs and DON'Ts just to remind you:

♦ Almost always, the rule is to wear uniform, but if you are living in, as a long-term carer, it goes without saying that you cannot wear uniform twenty-four hours a day. However when you are not on duty do not wander around the house in skimpy sexy clothes. Paula was amazed and shocked to be sexually harassed by the son of a patient for whom she was caring. However my surprise was much less when I learned that she had been wearing extremely suggestive clothing, and pattering around the house as if she were in her own home. The young man was stressed by the situation, and quite unused to seeing strangers in his home, and he reacted in a way that he himself was later shocked by.

The problem occurred when she was working a sleeping duty, and she was called to attend to her patient during the night. After she had settled her patient, she was accosted by the young man, who had also woken when he heard his mother call. The young man considered her to be a likely target, particularly since his own culture would never have permitted a woman to parade in front of men so scantily attired.

♦ While you are working never drink any alcohol, even if it is offered. It is unprofessional and can only lead you into trouble at some stage.

♦ The same with smoking. The laws have changed now, and smoking is no longer socially acceptable, so we are all more aware of the need to check the situation. Ask where you can smoke, either in the garden or perhaps the garage, and stick to lunch or coffee breaks to do so. Resist the temptation to join in if a visitor to the house is smoking, even if you are invited to do so.

♦ If your arrangement is that your patient will provide all meals, that is clear. If you are providing your own food, then it is all right for you to use tea and coffee, and perhaps a biscuit if they are set out for you, but do not eat the whole packet, or use up all the milk. Remember you are a guest in someone's home, and act as you would expect a guest to behave in yours.

♦ Never use anything from the fridge that may look as if it is special – like a piece of wedding cake, or some ice cream or strawberries. If there is something smelling bad, or mouldy, on view, check that you can remove it.

♦ Never use any facilities like the washing machine, unless it is specified in your contract, or if you are specifically offered it, or unless there is good reason. For example if you have been there unexpectedly for several days, and need a change of clothes, and cannot do a small amount by hand, ask first if it is all right, and the time is convenient.

♦ If you are coming in, or going out, always let your patient know, even if you are not on duty at the time. After a while you may not need to interrupt him, but initially keep him informed, as you come and go.

♦ Never invite friends in to visit you, unless you are actually living there for quite a while – for example, weeks at a time – and have a room of your own. Even then, always ask if it is possible. And make sure that you make no noise, and they leave early. This is important as this can cause major problems with patients.

♦ It is not acceptable to bring pets with you, even if the carer seems to like animals. Never try to baby-sit a child, even your own, and never invite a partner to stay overnight, however much you miss him, unless this is clearly offered in your contract. (It won't be!)

♦ Never borrow money from your patient, and make sure you record any shopping you do for him with a receipt.

♦ As we have seen already, it is nice to be offered gifts as a token of appreciation, and you can accept things like chocolates, and flowers, and even a theatre ticket, if someone cannot go. But never accept money, or expensive perfume, or jewellery. As we have already said, so often patients in a rush of affection and gratitude will offer a gift, and then regret it later, and if relatives ask where something has gone at a later date, you may be suspected of unprofessional behaviour, at the very least.

Also many people, when sick or old, have short memories, and can forget altogether. Do not put your reputation at risk. It is not uncommon for patients to request that you receive a gift when you finally leave, or after they die. Goodbye gifts are more acceptable, since they are usually given with some assistance from the family. Use your own discretion, always remembering that you must be able to account for anything you accept, if there is a problem later on.

♦ Be careful when using appliances or gadgets or crockery in another person's house. If you break something, report it immediately – be truthful and open, and if you can replace it, do so. Most people are quite understanding if there is accidental damage to their property, but if you are not honest about anything there will always be a residue of suspicion in the minds of the family, or the patient.

♦ It may be that you can work better if you alter the layout of a room. People who are ill often have no idea of the difficulties that arise from badly placed furniture, or a rug or carpet. Whatever is needed, take your time to look at the alternatives, and then sit down and explain to the patient or the family. Imagine someone coming to your house and telling you to start moving your chairs around; you might well give them a pretty sharp response. Explain and demonstrate, and don't be afraid to listen to alternative suggestions. If you, and your patient, are happy with the result, you will find it easier to do your job.

♦ You may need to answer the phone while you are in your patient's home. If you can do this clearly, it will save irritation on the part of the caller, and the patient. We all have our preferences. I like to hear someone give the maximum information, as in "Mrs Green's telephone, Jane Adams answering for her." You may prefer to give the name, or number. Do it clearly, and check with your patient about what they would like you to say.

♦ Never discuss your patient in intimate detail with other callers, especially friends. It is fine to say whether they have had a good night or enjoyed their lunch, or liked a particular television programme. It is not fine to pass personal comments about anyone in the household. Never say anything about anyone that you would not say to the person herself. The same rule applies to gossip about other carers, their practice or their personal lives. If you have a comment, save it for your manager, or if you have good reason, make it directly to the person concerned.

♦ In general you should not give your home phone number to the patient. When you are not at work, he should contact you through your employer. Sometimes the patient, or the family, attempt to make a private agreement with the carer, thus avoiding paying a commission to the employer. This is absolutely understandable, but it is defrauding your employer, and you are unwise to be tempted. You have good personal reasons, apart from loyalty to your employer. One is that you will not be covered for any mistakes you make, unless you have taken out professional insurance yourself. Another is that you may find the family become very demanding, and it can be hard to refuse. Leslie found this to her cost when her patient took to phoning her at all times, because they discovered she lived very close to them, and could be there within a few minutes. They called for minor reasons, like difficulty in moving the patient, when they needed a spare hand, or when the carer was delayed, or even for a "pop in" short visit while they went shopping. She began to feel harassed. The real problem came when they called her after the patient fell over, and she was out, so they called several times, only finally calling the agency for advice, as a last resort. The patient was quite badly hurt, and the whole story came out, because they had left her on the floor for so long. They blamed Leslie, and when her manager heard the story, Leslie lost her job as a result. The moral of this story is: keep your job and your home separate, so that you work a shift defined by your manager, and everyone knows when you are off duty.

♦ Carers are often asked about relatives or friends, who may be ill. Carers can be regarded as experts in all fields. The patients will offer descriptions of symptoms or investigations, and ask you what you think. Be very careful. I was once asked, by someone I knew only very slightly, about her husband. The wife asked about the investigations for a lung disease that her husband was experiencing, which was attributed to his job. She seemed very calm and curious rather than worried or highly strung. Because of the details I was given, I advised her to telephone a professional helpline, which would give her far more up-to-date information than I could.

I later realised that she was very distressed about the whole idea of a helpline, because she had not realised the details she had been given could be indicating a very serious complaint. I was never able to talk over the misunderstanding with her. I have never tried to offer that kind of help since. I only offer a helpline if asked specifically about one.

♦ It is not always possible to like everyone you work for. If it is difficult to hide the fact that you simply do not like your patient, and detect that the feeling is mutual and cannot be resolved, then ask your manager to move you before this causes a problem. If you can work through your dislike, it may surprise you later on to find that the awkward person has become someone you like very much indeed.

Chapter Eleven

Appropriate responses to different cultures and emotions

Most carers today will have to deal with many different cultures and religions in the course of their work. Many carers ask for guidelines about what they should do, or not do, in homes where the culture of the family is quite new to the carer. This is a subject that we will cover again in more detail, when we are talking about what to do when someone dies.

In fact, if you are meeting someone from a different culture, you cannot prepare yourself in a way that will cover all eventualities. It is best to get a rough idea of what beliefs they might hold by asking them, and then continue to ask, as you get to know the family. It is impossible to know what are strict rules, and what are preferences, unless you ask, and someone tells you.

For example, many cultures do not expect handshakes, especially from women. So knock at the door, smile when it opens, introduce yourself clearly and give your name, and see what the response seems to be. At some stage, you will have the opportunity to ask someone.

When you are planning your care, again ask the patient. What do you like me to do? How do you like me to do this? Especially when washing, or giving personal care for your patient, and especially when dealing with the opposite sex. In hospital the same rule applies.

Similarly when you are planning a meal, or shopping for food, your patient will tell you what he wants, and if he has a religious reason, for example eating only kosher food or halal meat, he will tell you. You only need to be aware that this may happen, and to ask if you are not sure. In fact, most people with strict food rules relating to their faith will not want you to cook for them, and will tell you exactly where to shop for their food, if they ask you to do so.

Most religious people (and many non-religious people) are deeply offended by the use of bad language, or sexual innuendo, and anyway it is not a professional way to communicate. Be sure that you do not use inappropriate language that can offend people, whatever you do in your own home.

Many older people are offended by words that are now commonplace in a younger group of people. Be careful about your language. This is also important if you are filling in a report. Use professional language, write clearly, and keep it short and to the point. You do not know who will be reading what you are writing. It is a record, and is a legal document. It is also the right of the patient to read what you have written.

Most people like to explain their preferences, or their religious customs. Few of them will be reluctant to talk, if they understand that you want to meet their needs, and are asking out of genuine interest. And if you are interested in people, and want to do this job and enjoy it, the more you learn, the more enjoyment you will find, in doing the work. And as you begin to understand one person, you will feel more confident in dealing with other people, who also have different ideas and beliefs. You may also find that you are not so far away from them, in the way you think, and what you believe in.

The general rule, as we have said, is to wear uniform all the time. If you wear casual clothes, make sure they are neat and not revealing. The young man in Chapter 10, who became sexually interested in the carer, is not an isolated example. Even if he had come from a different background, and was used to seeing casual dress at home, he might have responded to her in a similar way.

When a family, or a member of a family, is under stress, any or all of them can behave in a way that is not always normal or usual for them. For both men and women, sex can be a great release of tension, and if it seems to be on offer, they may take advantage, where they would never have done so in another situation.

There can also be misunderstandings when young males or females are handicapped in some way. Mary was caring for the wife of a married couple, who were both deaf from birth. Ann was dying, and her husband Bill was suffering greatly, as his wife became less able to communicate, as she grew less well. Mary had always had a very great empathy for those living with this particular handicap, and she spent a lot of time trying to communicate with the couple. One thing to remember about people who are deaf, or have communication problems because of illness or disease, is that you do not need to shout at them. Mary had learned to speak slowly and clearly and quietly – moving her lips in a slightly exaggerated way, and she could just about hear and lip-read what Ann was saying, almost up until she died. She acted as the interpreter for Bill, who was very distressed but was grateful to be able to lip-read Mary, as she repeated what she could hear from Ann. Mary felt privileged to have been with them at such a time, and was glad to have been of use in such a sad situation.

After Ann died, she called to say goodbye to Bill, and was amazed and very upset when he behaved in a very familiar way with her. A week later, he appeared at her house with some flowers, having looked her up in the phone directory, and made a few enquiries. She was uncomfortable enough to contact the Royal National Institute for Deaf People, telephone number 0808 808 0123, who were able to find someone who could talk to her about the way Bill might be seeing her. She had not realised that, having had little contact with hearing people, he was deeply touched by her attitude and compassion, and unable to hear the *tone* of her conversation he mistook the *words* and her sympathetic manner, and thought she was ready to start a romance with him. Desperate for company, after losing his wife, he thought he had found a suitable replacement. She had to explain very clearly to him, and he was very hurt, and she felt very guilty. She realised that if someone cannot hear you, you have to be very careful about how you communicate with them, so that they know what your intention is, and there are no misunderstandings.

Anyone who is not used to receiving kindness and understanding care from a virtual stranger, and is therefore particularly emotionally vulnerable at the time, may mistake your motives. This can lead to misunderstandings and inappropriate responses. If someone has not had too much support in a new and frightening situation, and along you come, to ease the burden and to help in a most practical way, it can be in a way that he almost "falls in love". He cannot be blamed for that, and you must be patient and learn to protect him. Most patients will praise their carers to the hilt, and that is gratifying for the carer, and pleasant to hear. Not many people will go to such an extreme, but you should be aware that it can happen. Do not let all the praise go to your head. There is no such person as the perfect carer.

There is another situation when problems in communication can lead to trouble. There are those who have lost their power of speech through a stroke or illness like multiple sclerosis or motor neurone disease, or even those with a very severe stutter, who may take a lot of time to produce a sentence. The temptation is to finish off the sentence for them. Do not do it. These people are not mentally handicapped in any way and if they feel patronised the patient can get so angry and frustrated that he finds it impossible to attempt any further conversation with you. Just be very, very, patient. If there is a close family member there, she/he can often help out. If not, then you simply have to be very patient. If the patient is using any aid to help with speaking, be interested enough to see how it works, and how you can quickly learn to read it or hear it.

Also, of course, there are a few people who will take advantage of other people (especially if you are female), in any situation, and you must follow your instincts about how to respond. As long as you have behaved in a non-provocative way, you should make your position clear, and never tolerate behaviour that makes you uncomfortable. Be absolutely clear from the first meeting that you are there to care for the sick, that your manager knows exactly where you are, and that you will leave immediately if you are experiencing any untoward behaviour. The best advice is to deal immediately with the problem, even if the offence is simply in the form of suggestive remarks; never collude with the speaker, do not laugh at all, and always stop the conversation at once. You may feel you are being a killjoy, but you will not be likely to get yourself into a difficult situation.

Gina, working for the first time with an attractive, successful and confident man who was partially paralysed, was quite flirty and chatty, and he felt confident enough to start pushing the boundaries with her. He first asked her to dry his chest with the hair dryer, as he still felt damp in that region. He was a very hairy man, so she agreed reluctantly, and was then propositioned for further services. She became very upset, and very angry. She learned later that he had a reputation for this kind of behaviour, and many carers, and nurses also, were so sympathetic to this charming person in his sad situation that they also were propositioned. It can be very distressing indeed even if you are quite worldly, and feel able to cope with any situation.

Never, however friendly towards you the family appears to be, never ever encourage flirting or teasing behaviour. You can only risk being the cause of arguments and distress, and adding to the family grief at this very difficult time. If Gina had anticipated his requests early on, she might have done some research on his problem, and been able to offer some advice or telephone numbers, which might have helped him to deal with his frustration himself appropriately.

Gay occasionally came across the bereaved husband of a lady she had nursed some months before, and after she had exchanged casual chat with him several times agreed to meet for a drink. Even though she had been quite unaware of his interest in her all those months earlier, when they began to see each other seriously she was appalled to learn that his family believed she had had designs on him long before his wife had died.

Once she realised that he had been aware of her long before, she felt very guilty and uncomfortable, and it was a long time before she was able to meet him comfortably and without guilt.

It is not uncommon for the relative of a person who is dying to form an attachment for the person most involved in giving care. It is a very emotional time; the nurse or carer, if sympathetic, will be a godsend to the family, and it is easy for someone who is about to be bereaved to fall a little bit in love with such an angel. He cannot see you, warts and all. Be very careful to do nothing to encourage the emotion. At a later stage you may meet again, and the attraction may still be there, but it is very likely you will meet again, and realise that you have absolutely nothing in common, and never will have.

It is less common, but not unknown, for the dying person to encourage her partner to think of replacing her with someone whom they know and like, like the nurse or carer. Peter was told by his wife, "Jean would make such a lovely wife for you, and all the family like her, and she knows all about the way you like things done. I wouldn't mind at all if you married her after I die."

Jean did not appreciate the suggestion, and found the whole idea upsetting and demeaning.

Even if there is no romantic attraction, you will find that families often seem unaware that you will leave, when the job is over; in other words when the patient dies or recovers. Be sure that you do not give the impression that you will stay in contact forever. It is too easy to show interest when someone says, "You would love our holiday house in Norfolk. You must come there for a break one day – we would so love to see you again."

Try to be non-committal, but still show interest. Show real enthusiasm, and he will remember it, and you will feel under pressure. For your own sake you need to keep your work life separate, and if many of the people for whom you care die, you cannot do bereavement support work in your spare time for everyone. Better to allow them to move on to another service, and a new life.

So do not risk adding to the pain of loss for the family with the new pain of betrayal. Do your job from a point of sympathetic detachment, and you will do it well.

All this may seem very theoretical. You need not contemplate all these situations arising each time you meet another patient. Maybe you will never experience most of these situations, but if you are aware of the possibility of any problems, you will pick up on emotional responses early and you will be less likely to have serious problems of this sort. Anticipating problems should increase your confidence, not make you apprehensive or suspicious.

When people are isolated in one room for most of the time, they often become expert people-watchers. I have been amazed at the observations made by those who seem totally wrapped up in their own lives, but who have come to conclusions about feelings, and emotions, and the lives of various carers, whom I know quite well, but who have never discussed such details with me. I have been told, she/he is not very happily married; I think she/he has had a bad childhood; she/he doesn't like her/his sisters/brothers/in-law; I think she/he is very hard-up; so-and-so has a very bad temper I think.

It is easy to reply, with honesty, that I have absolutely no idea of their personal circumstances. But there have been a few occasions when I was made more aware of my colleagues' circumstances, and tried to offer them support, which would not have occurred to me on my own.

Women especially, as we have seen, are curious about other people. Imagine being confined to one room, with no control over the stimuli you have, when your own life is on hold, and you may not feel ill, just bored, and restless, and frustrated, and, suddenly, you have the opportunity of talking with someone new, perhaps from a different culture, doing a job that you have never thought about. Any daily visitor, who does all the personal care for you, is a source of interest and speculation, and most of us would have similar responses. Try to offer some stimulus, be open to the exchange of information, but do it without getting too involved.

Chapter Twelve

Anticipating death

When you have been with several people, as they approach death, you will begin to develop a sense for when their time is running out. However, on the first occasion you may feel as nervous as your patient and family do. You need to remember that they will be depending on you to do the right thing, and if you think through the experience beforehand, it will help you to make decisions and recognise various stages of the whole process. You can then be more confident about what to do, if anything.

Every death is as individual as is each person. If you can talk about it with the family beforehand you will become used to thinking about it, and so will they. Hopefully this will take away some of the fear that may surround them at this time. Try to ask some relevant questions over the period before the death is imminent. It is much easier if you have been visiting the family/patient for long enough to get to know them all quite well. Of course, very often this will not be the case, and you may not have time to get to know them well enough, and then, as always, you must follow the feelings of the family, even if you think that sounds strange. Some people will want you to touch the patient, to stay with her/him, and to lead the way generally. Some will want you to leave at once. If you stay calm and supportive, it will help everyone to decide on what to do, when to do it and how much help they would like from you. Most of all, with your support, they will be able to make decisions without pressure.

You may find that the relatives you meet will start the conversation by telling you they are nervous about caring for someone at home, or the situation reminds them of a previous loss. Then it's easy to follow on and find out what are their real concerns.

If you do have the time to talk about it, what kind of questions should you ask? "Is this the first time you have ever been around someone who is so ill?" "Do you know what to expect when someone dies?" "Have you ever been with someone when they die?"

If you initiate the conversation do so very, very carefully. Written down, the questions seem bald and quite abrupt. However if you ask in a gentle way, and not as if you are going to interrogate them, or think them foolish, they may be glad to have the chance to talk about it. It is also important that the person you are talking to has already considered that this patient may be dying. Sometimes families are simply quite unaware of the possibility of death, even with very old and sick relatives.

"Have you talked to your doctor about whether he wants to come out if X dies?"

This is useful to know. Sometimes a GP will be happy to come out to certify the death, but if the death is expected, he may say he will come in the morning, after surgery begins. If the family know that, they will know whether to call him or not. Also, if they are expecting him to call they will not be disappointed.

"Do your family want to be called if X seems to be getting weaker and we think it is time?"

The middle of the night is no time to start trying to call any family to ask if they want to be there. If it has been discussed beforehand, there is no last-minute panic.

"Have you thought about the funeral, or which funeral director might be used?"

This is something that can be decided weeks ahead of the person dying. Funeral charges can vary quite a lot, and if they are called in the middle of the night, undertakers may charge more than for a daytime call. If the family decide to keep the person in the home till daybreak, there is the opportunity to have other family see the body at home, and also to arrange for it to be collected after the morning rush hour, for example, or after the schools have started, which may seem less public for the family.

"Does X know she/he is dying? Has X been told?"

"What would you like me to do if X dies while I am here?"

Of course you ask these kinds of questions over a period of time – you don't rattle them off in an inquisition as soon as you arrive. And if you ask these questions you must of course have some answers for the family, so we will look at some of the alternatives now.

For many people, dying is associated with blue lights and a 999 call. This may be because of television examples, or perhaps that has been their experience in the past. When someone is expected to die, it is not appropriate to call out the resuscitation team, and doing so can cause a lot of distress, and may even result in a frantic dash to the hospital, only to arrive with a dead body. In that case the dead person will be deposited at the mortuary at the hospital, whereas, in fact, the family may wish the body was at home. The ambulance team will not know that this is an expected death and if the patient is young and looks healthy, they will respond to the demands of the family.

Carol was with her daughter and a neighbour when she

suddenly went into respiratory collapse and a 999 call was made. She knew breathing complications were a recognised part of her illness so she had asked her husband Mack to make sure that no 999 calls would happen. Sadly, she and her husband had not *clearly* explained this to Tracy, her daughter, who was only seventeen years old. Mack was out, and her problems came on suddenly, and initially were unrecognised. When Tracy panicked and dialled 999, the ambulance men tried to resuscitate her, and then rushed her to hospital. Mack was distraught when he returned home to find she had been taken there. Tracy felt she had caused all the problems, and of course the hospital did not return Carol's body to her home, even though she was dead when she arrived at the hospital. Mack felt that all their talking and planning had failed Carol at the very end of her life.

So asking questions might clarify the plans of the family, and may even allow them to examine options they had not previously considered.

You may be sure that everyone will have wondered what they should do, how it would happen, and who to call when it does, but all too often no one talks about it. The question "Do you want to talk about what to do if/when X dies?" may be greeted with a sharp "No!" If that is the case then leave the question, because at some stage someone who does want to know what to do will almost assuredly come back to you, and want to talk about it.

Talking about it gives everyone a chance to air their views, and almost always avoids arguments later. It also gives you, the carer, the chance to reassure the family that it can all be managed as well as possible, so that there are no repercussions and regrets afterwards. Being open about it also removes some of the fear. You may feel that this is a very blunt question. As I said earlier, I feel that you can ask almost anything of people if you ask in the right tone.

If you ask this kind of question in a gentle sympathetic way, the shock is lessened and is not threatening. Giving voice to such anxiety can be a support.

If you do not feel you can ask these questions, then you must not, because you must feel confident to listen, and continue an open discussion. If you *can* do this sensitively, you will be performing a great service to the family.

Being open to discussion like this also gives a clear signal to a family that they can ask you other difficult questions. Remember it is important that you are honest in your replies, and in your opinions, at all times.

A very common question asked of carers is "Do you believe in God?" because many people think that if you are with sick people a lot, you will consolidate your beliefs in heaven and hell, and life after death, and the existence of God, and all the other related questions.

If you are asked this question, it is not an opportunity for you to make a conversion to your own particular subscribed belief. I would never say to anyone that in my view there is no God, or indeed that there is one, because I do not know. I would say that I do not believe that death is the end of love, or the love between people. If someone asked me to read a passage from the Bible or another religious book, I would be glad to do this, and I have done it on occasion. I would never denigrate a belief, however unrealistic I feel it to be, if it is comforting to someone nearing the end of life. But equally, it is not the time to attempt a religious conversion, as this kind of pressure will usually result in a change of subject, and a reluctance to resume the discussion at a later stage.

If you are asked a question, and you do not know the answer, or simply have none to offer, say so. If it is relevant, you can say you will try to find out, and do so, but honesty is *always* the best policy.

So, whatever you can do to prepare the family for the

approaching death is going to be useful. And, if they can begin to talk about their feelings, and make some plans and identify some expectations, you will have done a good job, and they will probably continue the dialogue after you have left.

When someone dies, you may find that the family become very upset, and you must decide whether to stay and support them, or leave them to some privacy. Again, if you have any doubts then ask them what they want. "Would you like me to go now – what would you rather I do?"

As you become more experienced, you will be able to reassure people that most deaths are peaceful, and you will be able to explain some of the physical changes that occur, so that the family know what to expect, and are not apprehensive about staying with their family member. If people are confident that they know what to do, they are better able to support each other, and after it is all over, they will feel glad that they were there.

If there is a palliative care team involved, they should make the last few days much more comfortable. But all teams are different. You are the patient's advocate, and if the sick person does not feel happy with the service offered, they must understand that they do not have to accept it. This is when you must remain detached – whatever you feel about the other professionals involved, you must act only for the patient and family. Try to avoid any arguments and confrontations. But remain the advocate of the patient, who is going to need all your support.

Sometimes this is hard to do – to remain detached in the centre of such high levels of emotion. This is especially hard in the family home, when the family are unlikely to feel any need for restraint, and may resort to old family arguments simply because they are stressed and scared.

Always try to calm the situation, and to keep the family focused on what is best for the patient. This is such an important time in the life of the whole family, as well as the sick person. Do not let them forget this, because they will have to live with the effects of this period for long afterwards.

There will be people who will say that dying is a specialist service, and specialists can become very possessive about their patients. This chapter is not designed to make you into a specialist. But dying is something we all will do one day, and as long as your approach is gentle and thoughtful, with the patient and the family at the centre of everything you do, and as long as you feel comfortable with speaking to them, I believe anyone can be a great support.

You will find that understanding the process of dying, and supporting a family as well as the sick person through the experience, will change you as well. Most people give little thought to dying, though we most certainly all will do so, and your experiences will benefit you and your family more than you can imagine.

Chapter Thirteen

What happens when someone dies?

When a death is expected, we usually observe a slow deterioration over a period of time. The sick person sleeps more, is less interested in eating and drinking, and does not seem to be "present" for a lot of the time. She/he will answer questions briefly or not at all, and show little interest in conversation, except in short bursts fading quickly.

We know a lot about what is happening physically with the dying. Caring for them is simplified, as they need only to be kept comfortable, clean and in a calm environment. We also know that hearing is one of the last senses to leave them, so whatever you do for that person, you must talk quietly, and explain as you go along.

"Hello, Jane, it's Anna here, and I have come to wash you and change your sheets. I am going to start by taking the covers off like this, and will make sure that you are not cold by keeping this blanket over you. We also have the fire on so you should be fine. It's a lovely day – I hope you can hear the birds, etc., etc."

Just talk as if you are having a conversation – taking a long pause occasionally, as you would do, if she or he were answering you. Do not feel that you must keep up an endless rattle – do what feels comfortable.

We know that lack of fluids exacerbates the problem of a dry mouth, and so when someone is unable, or is reluctant to swallow, we need to moisten their mouth frequently. Show the family how to do this so they can continue the care when they are alone. You will almost always find that even an apparently unconscious person will suck at a damp sponge because of a dry mouth. Hopefully the nurses will have left some small mouth sponges for the carers to use. But be gentle. Remember, or imagine, how unpleasant it is to have something forced into your mouth, as may have happened when you were small. Your patient will dislike it as well. And of course do not pour liquids into the mouth of someone who appears to be almost unconscious.

You can use a dry baby's brush to clean teeth, and again it is not uncommon to find that a semi-conscious person will co-operate with cleaning teeth because it makes the mouth feel better. Most mouth washes taste fine, but do little more than taste clean, and if you can actually make a mouth cleaner you will be doing a good job for your patient. You cannot use mouthwashes on a semi-unconscious person, but you can use a damp brush or sponge. Even if false teeth have been removed, the mouth will still be better for being cleaned.

You may well find that a "top and tail" wash is sufficient for someone who is very weak and fragile, and hates being moved. Clean sheets and pillowcases are wonderfully refreshing to look at, as well as lie in and on.

Be sure that any time you turn someone over you are especially gentle, and that you explain yourself clearly, and avoid sudden jolts, which cause them to become agitated or feel insecure.

More than anything, you must remember that you are there for the family now, as much as you have ever been there for the patient. *This is especially not the time to promote your own religious views, tempting as it may be for you.* If the family want to talk about religion with you, then offer a *brief* summary of what you believe, and say no more. If they ask you questions, answer them. Be sure that your own desire to convert or convince someone does not blind you to the needs they have at this time. Many people remember with anger and distress being harassed by outside carers at such a time. If you want to say a prayer to yourself at any time, that is your right, of course, but keep it to yourself, and respect the wishes of the family.

As they near death, many people develop heavy and loud breathing, almost like a snore. They may be quite unaware of this, and even think it is coming from outside. I knew of one old lady who thought the sink was blocked. Explain to the family that the noise usually distresses the observers more than it does the patient. The doctor can relieve this to an extent, but often medication adds to the dryness of their mouth, may take time to arrange, and also may be given by injection, so try to help by changing the position of the patient before asking for medication.

Lying someone on one side, or raising the head a little, can make a difference. Also, a regular change of position helps to prevent the skin becoming sore and bruised, which can happen quite quickly as the circulation slows, and the patient is receiving very little nourishment and fluids. When you move someone, it is often comforting for them to receive a very gentle massage with some oil or cream on the area upon which they have been lying for the last hour or so.

You may notice that the person stops breathing altogether, and after several seconds, sometimes even minutes, starts again. (Everyone present usually stops breathing as well for a short time.) However this is a normal process, so do not let the family become panicky. It is a stressful time, because it feels as if the person is dying every time. Try and keep everyone calm. This stage can be likened to a battery slowly losing power, and intermittently failing altogether. It is not something to be frightened by.

It is also quite common for people to become very restless, and tug at the bedclothes incessantly. This can be very distressing to watch, and can be treated with medication. Betty, watching her husband die, with their children coming and going in the room, explained to the children that he was in character, as he was always agitated if he was travelling anywhere. However at times it can be very distressing to watch, and needs to be relieved. If the palliative care team are involved, the problem will hopefully have been addressed and anticipated. If not, the GP should be asked to help specifically with that problem.

It is important that the patient is not in pain, and medication is sometimes stopped, because the patient appears to be unconscious and the suggestion is that they will not feel pain. However, this is not always so, and there are painless ways of giving medication, if someone cannot swallow. It is safer to continue with the medication to relieve pain until death occurs. Problems with swallowing are often the reasons that medication is discontinued. Encourage the family to ask the doctor for help if the person cannot swallow. This does not mean feeding them by tube, they no longer need to eat, but there are other ways to give the medication they need.

Relatives often worry because the patient feels cold to touch, and they want to wrap their loved one up and keep her/him warm. Of course we must not let patients feel cold, so if they start to become restless or shiver, then by all means add a cover or two. However, usually patients seem unaware of feeling cold, and as long as they seem comfortable there is no need for concern. As they become weaker they may well become sweaty and clammy, and as part of their care they can be gently sponged to refresh them.

Often at the end of a life the body becomes discoloured – almost appearing bruised. This can be easily understood, as a running down of the system – the battery example helps here too, because as the system slows, and body fluids stop draining away properly, the blood circulation also does the same, and so gradually causes the discolouration.

It is generally good practice to keep the room light and well aired – especially if it is nice weather, and the sounds outside are not too harsh and raucous. For someone who has lived in a town throughout life, the sound of police cars and heavy traffic is familiar, and not intrusive. Likewise a country dweller will be used to birdsong and country noises. A person who is dying does not have to be in a dark room, in heavy silence, with whispering all around. Dying is only another part of life, and we do not have to exclude the person who is experiencing this final act. So encourage everyone to talk normally, and to include the dying person in the conversation.

Similarly, a young person who has a young family will usually not be at all fazed by the familiar noises of children playing, even if appearing unconscious for most of the time. Paula, who had just become a new young granny, had her baby granddaughter lying on her lap for several hours before she died, and everyone who saw her felt aware of her contentment. She wanted to be alive for the birth of the baby, and once she heard of the safe arrival, she appeared to lapse into unconsciousness, but was not at peace until the child, only a few hours old, was placed on her lap. With her hand gently resting on the baby she slept peacefully until she died.

Whatever the family feel moved to do, encourage them, whatever your personal feelings or beliefs are, unless of course it is obviously unsafe for some reason.

Encourage the family to include everyone. We have developed a practice of excluding children from life events, because we think they may be scared. At one time childbirth and death were part of the pattern of life, and everyone was aware when either event occurred. We are becoming more open about birth in many ways, but death is still shrouded in euphemisms.

Reuben, when told by his granddad that they had "lost" the family dog, was puzzled as to why they didn't go and find it. He finally asked, "Do you mean that the dog is dead?" Quite logically, a child may be concerned that if dogs can get lost, then so can people, and no one wants to think that someone will not go looking for them, if they should get lost one day.

Amy, who was very small when her mummy died, seemed to understand, and accept, that Mummy had gone to heaven. Several years later she was taken on holiday to Devon, and really believed her mummy would be there for her waiting.

It is better to be honest, and say that someone has died. It reinforces the realisation that a death has occurred, which euphemisms do not. If the family do not agree with this, then you have to accommodate their wishes, but if you give the explanation for the preference for honesty, they may well change their minds. Always remember that they are feeling their way, and this is a very new experience for them, and it is painful to learn about death firsthand. Whatever support and help you can offer will be valued.

Always offer to stay with the dying person, but make it clear that you will do what the family want. They may like to have you, just to help with the physical care, and then expect you to leave them when you have finished that care. In that case make sure that you stay out of the way, but are around to talk or make a drink, or whatever is needed. Keep reminding them that hearing is the last sense to go, and so they can continue to talk to the person as they have always done.

If someone is alone with a dying relative, make special efforts to see that they eat something, and are looking after themselves. This is a sad time to be alone – and they will need particular support and awareness from you.

Sometimes very significant conversations take place at this late stage, and people find peace and perhaps reconciliation when they least expect it.

When death finally happens, there is often an outburst of emotion, and you may find it hard to keep your own feelings under control. It is not unreasonable to find that you have tears in your eyes for the painful emotion that may be released in you. However, this is not your moment, and one shared tear is the maximum you can allow yourself. Concentrate on supporting the family. Give them time to cry and to do whatever they need to do. Make the tea, and hand out tissues. You can relieve your feelings with a good cry, or a large gin, or say your own prayers, when you are in the privacy of your own home.

Fairly soon, you will find they will be ready to do something, but they may wonder what.

Of course, if you have had the time to talk it through with them they will know roughly what to do next. As you know, the doctor must certify death before you can call the funeral directors. He must be informed at once unless there is a previous arrangement that the family will wait until morning. If you start laying the body out, without informing him, however minimally, the doctor may complain that you have diagnosed the death for him. So, deal with the legalities first. If he or she is not surprised by the phone call, and is going to take a long time to come, then you may like to tidy the bedroom up a little, and remove the covers, leaving the place tidy and uncluttered, so the family can continue to sit and talk. Encourage them to talk about what has happened, and to recall the good memories.

If the doctor has been informed, and is coming, discuss

with the family what they would like you to do. If you have to go off duty, then talk through with the family about what they can do and what feels comfortable for them. Do they want you to wash the body if you are there, and if not, do they feel all right about doing it themselves? It is not practice to give the body a thorough washing, but many people like to feel that a loved one is clean and fresh when they leave the house. The funeral director will do the proper preparation on going back to the funeral home.

If the doctor has previously said he will not be attending till morning, then note the time the person finally stopped breathing, and write it down. Then you can usually tidy up, wash the body, and clear the room a little.

Whatever you do, ask the family if anyone wants to help you. Very often someone would like to, but is nervous, and will be glad to help, with some support. If they want to be alone, then leave them. Whatever you have to do, treat the body with respect and gentleness, and talk quietly if you have to explain what you are doing. Never forget that this body, much loved, or even if not much loved by the family, is very significant for them.

As we have said, even if no family members want to help, they may appreciate the idea of your giving the body a wash and tidy up, to clean any body fluids away. Comb the hair, put the false teeth in if necessary. Make sure the mattress is protected, in case any leaks from the body continue to occur. All that needs doing then is to make sure that they can easily reach the body, and that the room is tidy and cool.

If the funeral directors are not coming until perhaps the morning, or the family want to wait for another relative to call first, it is not usual to cover the face, and it is often a nice touch to put the hands outside the sheet, and place some flowers in them. The aim is to make the room look as normal as possible, with curtains open and the place tidy

– with of course the usual proviso that this is what the family is happy with.

When you have tidied up, you may find that the family would prefer to be alone, and so make it easy for them by asking occasionally if all is well, or if they want you to leave. If you are sensitive they will be able to tell you, and you can then go, feeling that you have done a good job for your patient and family.

What to tidy

♦ Any dirty washing – put in the appropriate place.
♦ Washing materials, bowls etc.
♦ Any glasses, stale drinks etc. from the patient.
♦ Anything cluttering the floor – shoes etc. belonging to the patient.
♦ Bedpans, commodes, walking frames etc., which make the room appear like a sick room, and are no longer required.
♦ Drugs and medications. Gather them together with all the notes and records (in which you will also have recorded any care you have given and the time at which any doctor was called).
♦ In short make the room look as neat and finished as you can.
♦ If there are flowers around, it is nice to put them somewhere out of the way where they will still brighten the room.
♦ All the extra bedding needs to be out of the way, so there is just a sheet, and the body can air and cool a little, and will not exude any odours.

If arguments develop, try to remain calm and detached, and encourage everyone to do nothing in the heat of the moment. If you do nothing, there is less chance of bitter resentments at a later date.

Some people who are involved in caring for the dying on a regular basis carry with them verses or writings to comfort the family. If you do this there is a good website for those kind of writings: <www.poeticexpressions.co.uk>. These are very helpful to read for some people and there is a variety to choose from. I have known of relatives who have kept these verses for many years after the death, and one family who used the same verse for the funeral of their second parent, who died in an accident months later.

Some carers try to pay a short visit to the remaining relative a week or so after the death, and when the funeral is over. If you have time this can be very helpful sometimes. It gives someone the chance to go over the last few days of the person's life, and ask questions or make comments, and the carer can reassure or explain any queries. Sometimes this is not appropriate. Follow your instincts, but realise that this goodbye is the final one for you. You must expect that the person you are leaving may be rather emotional, as any goodbyes are hard for them at this stage. It may be hard for you as well, having been with them at such a time. So do it to the best of your ability without giving the impression that you will be back at some time.

Chapter Fourteen

Helping the family to make difficult decisions

If you spend some time in a close family environment, it is almost inevitable that at some point you will become involved in discussions about issues like treatment, diet, and even family arguments. We have discussed this in a previous chapter, and will take a closer look at the problem now. This is a time when an outsider can either support the family through discussion, or exacerbate the situation and increase the arguments. What is the best way to handle the situation?

Like many of the other issues we have discussed in this book, there can never be a concrete solution to this kind of situation. The best way to manage to keep the peace is by keeping calm, encouraging the family to air their opinions, and talk things through.

Let us look at the example of a family argument. There are some general rules to observe. The really important thing to remember is that you are the patient's advocate. You must be aware of any attempts to bully the person you have been employed to care for.

Apart from that, one stricture must always be adhered to. Never take sides. Encourage the family to keep all doors open. If there is no solution, and the family is absolutely polarised in their points of view, so that no one will give way, then one suggestion is to invite a counsellor to help mediate. Remember the family will have to live with the consequences of the dispute for the rest of their lives. You can remind them of this in a quiet unobtrusive way.

When someone is sick or dying, the emotions raised can surprise everyone, even if the family is not emotionally close. There are always issues of who did what, and how much, and in most families there is one workhorse, one who picks up the bills, one who is the all-time expert and inflexible in their knowledge, one who feels hard done by, and so on. If the sick member is the matriarch, or in some way has held the family together, then when that constraint has gone, or is diminished, the family can appear to start a war.

Any argument raises old quarrels, and feelings of being left out, or undervalued. If everyone is aware of this, they can try to alleviate those negative feelings. If you are aware of your own issues, you can stand back and observe what is happening. Most of us have regrets about our own lives; times when we wish we had made more allowances, said something different, controlled our responses, or just kept silent. Hearing similar family arguments can make us lose objectivity, and join in. If something really affects you, it is time to stop and consider why, because it will be your own history that causes the reaction, and not anything that happens in that family at that time. So, count to 100 rather than just 10 while you think about it, and you may find that you do not offer an opinion even then. The old saying "least said soonest mended" is still true. The other reason for not taking sides is that families may be used to squabbling and making up, and when the row is over they may turn on you as the scapegoat, and you may shoulder all the blame. After all, you are still the outsider.

Some really angry arguments can be about the medical treatment offered or not offered to the person who is sick. May was seventy-six, and her main problem was Altzheimer's disease. Her carer, Barbara, had nursed her own mother through the same thing, and she was very good at managing May at her most difficult. May had five children, who all cared greatly about her, and vied for "top dog" position, whenever decisions had to be made. But the oldest daughter, Ivy, a widow, had given up her job to live with her mother, and she felt she should have the final say in any treatment May was offered. May had some health problems, which were finally diagnosed as cancer of her womb or uterus. She was pretty healthy apart from her mental state, and surgery was a suggestion. Barbara had seen the effect quite minor surgery had had on her own mother, who did not understand or remember what she was told was happening to her, and whose mental state deteriorated rapidly in the few days she was admitted to hospital. Barbara felt that May was not suffering any severe symptoms, and should be left alone. Ivy wanted the operation for her mother. Ivy's daughter, however, was a nurse, and could not see that it would be of any benefit, but knew that Ivy, her mother, would lose her home, if her grandmother died. She was sure that was influencing Ivy's attitude, even unconsciously. The rest of the family lined up behind the main antagonists, and the arguments raged. The GP was ineffective at explaining the options, and with an increase in litigation within the health service he was not prepared to intervene, and thus be held responsible. A neighbour was finally able to get the family together, and initiate an interview with a geriatric consultant, who was very open-minded, and was prepared to spend the time outlining the options, and the probable effects on May.

The family finally decided to leave May as she was, unless surgery became urgent. She was treated for anaemia, and at one stage for an unrelated chest infection, but she became weaker, and finally she had an unexpected heart attack, and died very suddenly.

The family were very grateful that she had not had surgery, when, months after her death, they visited a nephew following his car accident, and saw for themselves an old lady in intensive care, who had had major surgery, and was terribly confused and demented, and quite terrified. They did understand that this might not have been the way May would have responded, but knowing her mental condition it was a probability, and they were glad she had not had to undergo the trauma of leaving her home, and having an anaesthetic and an operation.

Barbara could have perhaps helped in the decision more effectively, if she had been able to stand aside and ask a few questions. If the family asked the right questions, they may well have jointly come to a conclusion, based on understanding the way it might affect their mother. For example:

- What effect might the anaesthetic have on May?
- Would the GP want his own mother in the same situation to undergo the same surgery? Has that question been put to him?
- How much would May be able to understand about what was being done to her? How much did she understand about her life now? Would she be able to co-operate with the physiotherapist, for example, after the anaesthetic? How much did she co-operate now? If she did not co-operate wouldn't this make a difference to her rate of recovery?

- ◆ What kind of changes would the disease cause, if left alone to progress at the same rate? In other words, would May be likely to die of old age before the operation became necessary?
- ◆ Could the disease be controlled with medication? Even taking her pills was a cause of much dispute, since she was so confused.

The questions could not help Ivy with the problem of where she might live if her mother died, but that would have to be the next step, with some delicate questioning, and probing, and reassurance, from the siblings. After all, if May had deteriorated mentally, it might not have been possible to nurse her at home for very long, and the same problems would have arisen anyway.

When someone reaches the end of life, there are often differing opinions about treatment, especially in the case of cancer treatments, which might be traumatic, and perhaps painful. If the patient is aware, then she/he must have the main say in her/his care, but when not able to understand, or reluctant to discuss options, the family may be divided in their opinions. The professional carer is in the position of offering alternatives, or at least suggesting ways of finding the information to help make a decision.

Of course the family may not be able to settle the arguments, especially where fairly young people are involved, and sadly the death of a parent may only lead to family quarrels and disharmony, which can take years to resolve.

Some sources of information

Cancer BACUP (British Association of Cancer United Patients)

SPECIALIST ASSOCIATIONS:

Motor Neurone Disease Association
Altzheimer's Association
Carers Associations
Young Carers Association

Age Concern is listed in your local directory, and is very helpful usually. Your local directory also provides complete listings of helplines that cover virtually all eventualities.

As time goes by, you will be able to make your own list of the people who have been most helpful to you, and your advice will be more valuable to your patients and their families. But to begin with, you can use the nearest sources, like the district nurse or the Macmillan nurse. If there is not one of these specialists involved, then this is a good place to start.

Sometimes patients will use you as their voice, to explain their views to the family, or more likely to friends. Eva did this when she was due to go into the hospice for a nerve block, and to give her family a well-earned break. Her previous hospice stay was not effective, because her family visited every day, and stayed all day. In fact, Eva was exhausted by the time she went home. She had never had so many people round her bed. She privately suspected that many people came out of curiosity, to see what the place was like. Her family came because they were anxious that she did not feel abandoned, and also so that the staff did not think she was abandoned. They too became very tired trekking up to the hospice in rotation.

She confided in Naomi, her carer, that she would like this visit to be a rest, but didn't want to hurt anyone's feelings. Naomi was able to tell the family in a very gentle and pleasant way that Eva would prefer them to have a break and let her settle in without all the visitors. After the two weeks were over, Eva came home feeling much better, and full of stories about the people she had met, the things she had seen, and the many different activities she had enjoyed. She also became confident enough to be more sociable and comfortable meeting new people, which had not happened in her first stay, because she was so rarely alone. She felt rejuvenated by her stay, and so were her family. They planned on her next visit to go away on holiday.

Even in hospital, visiting can become too overwhelming. Of course it is awful not to have any visitors. But it is exhausting to have people by your bed for hours at a time. No one would dream of visiting someone for as long, or as often, as they visit in hospital. What is there to talk about, day after day, for hours at a time? Even if there is nothing at all wrong with you, such visits can be draining, let alone when you are feeling ill or weak. It is lovely to have cards, or small gifts, and a quick visit, but not often the marathons that many people have to endure, when they are hospitalised.

Sometimes the carer can explain the feelings of the patient more sympathetically than anyone else. And also explain the point of view of the family to the patient. However, you need to be careful that you do not interpret what people mean, and stay only with reporting what someone says, with their permission, of course. Your own feelings about what to do are not relevant.

Chapter Fifteen

People with AIDS and other transmittable diseases

For a long time people with the AIDS virus faced discrimination, from all sections of society, including many people in the medical profession. Fear was the main driving force for this response, because the disease was seen as a killer for a long time. Sadly, it is still so in many parts of the world but, for us in the West, this is no longer so. With advances in treatment, people will live for many years in the Western world with a positive HIV status.

When the virus was first identified, the main body of people affected by it were homosexual men. This fact frequently led to more discrimination, and many young men died, while governments and society seemed unaware, and uncaring, and families were absent either from shame, or because they were not informed of the situation. Young men who were not infected lived with ghosts to a large extent, as so many of their friends and lovers died in a short time.

Then other citizens were affected by blood transfusions from people who were unwitting carriers of the virus. They were immediately described as "innocent victims". Even today there is a remnant of this prejudice in society, and people are still labelled as "innocent" or "guilty" by uneducated people, according to how they became infected.

The fact is that if society begins to categorise people as "innocent " or "guilty" according to some moral judgement, we are in danger of losing any humanity, or quality of compassion that we still have left in society.

Now AIDS is spread over the whole of society, and in all regions. Drug-users have been recognised as a largely affected group, which was not understood in the very early days. But, for anyone infected, the guilt is still there, and the prejudice, and much of the fear.

Caron, in the early 1980s, as a student nurse, saw her first HIV-positive patient admitted following a road accident. The patient was a sixteen-year-old girl, who immediately informed the staff of her HIV status, for their own protection. She was then placed in a single room, and nursed by anonymous people, encased in masks and gloves and gowns, who said little to her, and rushed out of the room as quickly as possible. Even her food was served with gloved hands. As a student nurse, Caron had no choice but to do as she was instructed, but never forgot the experience, especially when, after two days, the girl was discharged, since her injuries were not serious, and she was last seen sitting outside her room waiting for the transport to take her home, and watching the ward staff fumigating the room she had vacated. She knew that that young girl would never be ready to return to hospital of her own free will, for any kind of further treatment, and who could blame her?

That was in the early days of the virus, and fortunately things have improved since then. However as carers in the community, we still have to accept some responsibility for the attitudes of the people we meet in our work day to day. It may seem an impossible task, but society will only change when ordinary people change their attitudes. Legislation does not change attitudes, but people on the ground can affect their work colleagues, and society will eventually change. So those of us who are in regular contact with people from all walks of life have some responsibility for those who may be vulnerable, and for whom we care. So be sure that you do not add to the prejudice in our society by what you say, because you never know who is listening, and what their experience of this virus has been.

There are many courses for carers to help them to understand the virus, so that we can care for sick people without any risk to ourselves, and our families, and of course our patients. AIDS is not the only disease in the community that is highly contagious. People with AIDS are very vulnerable to opportunistic disease such as tuberculosis. A simple cold virus may make a healthy person feel quite unwell, but may make a person with AIDS very ill indeed. So while we must be aware of the need to protect ourselves from contracting the virus, we must be equally aware of the danger we may pose to someone already infected.

The first thing to remember is that the AIDS virus is very fragile. It is easily destroyed by normal hygiene like hot water and soap, and lives for only a short while outside the body. If all you are doing is caring for someone already infected, it is almost impossible for you to become infected too, because careful cleaning away of any body fluids, or secretions, with hot soapy water, is enough to destroy the virus. Blood is the body fluid most associated with the virus. You will probably discover when you nurse people with AIDS that the patient is more aware than you are of any risk of passing on the virus. If you have any doubts, you can usually ask the patient, and be sure of receiving informed advice.

The danger is most real when people, because they are unaware of how the disease is spread, are careless when dealing with injury to strangers. In a shop once I cut my finger on something and bled profusely. The assistant rushed up with tissues and dressings, and assured me that she would do it for me. Bleeding quite heavily, I tried to tell her that she should not be cleaning up *anyone's* blood, and she was quite offended, and said that she was sure I was okay. As it happens, I do not have the virus, but how could she know that by my appearance? And more to the point, I might not know whether I was infected, having never been checked. The first rule is to take care with *any* body fluids. Never perform personal care, involving body fluids, without wearing gloves.

As we have said, HIV is not the most dangerous virus. There are many viruses and bacteria that in certain circumstances are dangerous to humans. Instead of trying to judge people by their appearance, it is sensible to treat everyone as though either one of you may be at risk. This is not being dramatic, it is just a sensible way to take care of yourself and your family, which is after all your main concern. In fact, it is a sensible precaution to assume that any person to whom you are giving personal care could have a transmittable disease. It is therefore sensible to treat with care any body fluids from all of the patients for whom you are caring. This is relevant in your daily life, as well as your work as a carer. If you have this attitude you safeguard yourself, those you love and anyone with whom you come into contact.

You do not have to wear a mask, and gloves, and carry your hygiene precautions to extremes in your day-to-day duties, but you do have to take care when you handle all body fluids. This means using gloves for handling urine, faeces, vomit, and blood. Any other form of contact is perfectly safe.

Initially, people with AIDS were an easily identified group, and we have seen that this is no longer the case. There is still a great deal of prejudice concerning the disease, and many people who are infected are terrified of the news becoming public. This especially applies to many women, often refugees from war zones, where the disease was transmitted by violent personal attack, usually rape. Through fear, many of these people have had no support or counselling. If you are caring for someone like this, you cannot become their counsellor, but you can offer tremendous support and love, simply by treating these people with compassion and gentleness, and without judgement. Do not forget that they are at more risk than you are from developing further illness. And with present medication, this disease is not the death sentence it was twenty years ago. You can make an extraordinary difference to them simply by accepting them with respect and kindness.

So we can see that because of the existence of the virus in the community, you must be aware of the possibility of one of your patients, of whatever age or sex, being affected by AIDS or by hepatitis. And act accordingly.

While on the subject of infectious diseases, just a reminder for you to keep all kitchen and bathroom surfaces clean. Food poisoning is common in the West, and can only be so common because care is not taken. Whether you are working at home with your family, or in a workplace not associated with illness of any sort, you are setting a standard, and an example to anyone observing you. Some of the homes you will visit will be neglected for many reasons, and therefore not as clean as yours may be. Taking care of your hygiene standards will ensure that your family and anyone else with whom you are in contact will be safe in your hands.